Contents

Overview

The *Screening, Diagnostic, Placement Assessment* book includes the following:
- Screening assessment information
- Diagnostic assessment information
- Oral Reading Fluency Assessment
- Informal Reading Inventory
- Placement Tests

Using Macmillan/McGraw-Hill TREASURES

The **TREASURES** assessments can be used to screen students and diagnose deficiencies in phonemic awareness, phonics, fluency, vocabulary, and comprehension. The National Reading Panel identified the following early reading skills to help teachers "Put Reading First":

Phonemic Awareness
- Hearing and identifying sounds in spoken words

Phonics
- Recognizing the relationship between written letters and spoken sounds

Fluency
- Reading text accurately, quickly, and with expression

Vocabulary
- Knowing the words to use to communicate effectively

Comprehension
- Understanding and deriving meaning from what has been read

Screening, Diagnosis, and Placement

For information about students' reading readiness or reading level, use a combination of one or more of the following assessments:
- DIBELS (K–3)
- TPRI (K–3)
- Fox in a Box (K–2)
- Oral Reading Fluency Assessment
- Informal Reading Inventory
- Placement Tests

Assessment and *No Child Left Behind*

The National Assessment Committee created an assessment framework that defines the four kinds of reading assessments that are essential in a scientifically-based reading program: screening, diagnostic, progress monitoring, and outcome. In this book we will address the first two kinds of assessments. We will show you how to screen your students and how to use diagnostic and placement information to identify what your students need to know.

Macmillan/McGraw-Hill TREASURES works within the *No Child Left Behind* assessment framework by incorporating screening and diagnostic assessments into our reading program:

- **Screening Assessments** are the first step in identifying students who may be at risk of academic failure. Screening assessments are brief procedures that usually take no more than one to ten minutes to administer. They focus on critical reading skills and are predictive of future reading growth. If a student is *not* identified as being "at risk," then there is no need to continue diagnostic testing at this level. This minimizes testing time for most students and eliminates unnecessary tests.

- Students who are identified as being at risk need to then move on to one or more diagnostic assessments. Screening assessments provide a quick way to rule out students who are likely to have no risk so that resources can be focused on further evaluation of those potentially at risk.

- **Diagnostic Assessments** are assessments that are designed to identify students' specific strengths and weaknesses. They are administered multiple times throughout the year, and are designed to help determine appropriate intervention strategies. They provide additional data to help tailor reading instruction to meet specific student needs.

- Diagnostic information also aids teachers in forming instructional groups of students with similar developmental needs. This enables teachers to customize their instruction and provide additional support to smaller groups of students at a time.

Screening Options

Screening Students K–3

Most states or school districts identify the screening assessment you should use with your students, such as DIBELS or TPRI. It is recommended that you use the approved screening assessment in your state to identify at-risk students. We provide the information needed to align both **DIBELS (pages 5–9)** and **TPRI (pages 10–12)** to **TREASURES** on the indicated pages.

DIBELS (Dynamic Indicators of Basic Early Literacy Skills), K–3

DIBELS are short, one-minute fluency measures. The probes are individually administered, and measure all of the following:

Reading First Component	DIBELS Measure	Grade Level
Phonemic Awareness	Initial Sound Fluency	K
	Phoneme Segmentation Fluency	K–1
Phonics	Nonsense Word Fluency	K–1
Fluency (Connected Text)	Oral Reading Fluency	1–3
Comprehension	Oral Reading and Retell Fluency	1–3
Vocabulary	Word Use Fluency	K–3

TPRI (Texas Primary Reading Inventory), K–3

The TPRI probes are individually administered, quick, and given at the beginning, middle, and end of the year. They measure all of the following:

Reading First Component	TPRI Measure	Grade Level
Phonemic Awareness	Blending: On-set-Rimes, Phonemes	K–1
Phonics	Graphophonemic Knowledge	K–1
	Word Reading	K–3
Fluency (Connected Text)	Reading Accuracy and Fluency	1–3
Comprehension	Listening/Reading Comprehension	K–1/1–3

Screening Students 4–6

For screening students in the upper grades, we have provided an **Oral Reading Fluency Assessment** on **pages 25–64**. Fiction and nonfiction passages are provided along with comprehension questions. The screening assessment should be administered three times a year to measure students' fluency in the fall, winter, and spring.

Using DIBELS for Screening

What is the DIBELS screening assessment?

- Dynamic Indicators of Basic Early Literacy Skills measures reading acquisition skills.
- DIBELS provides an indicator of how well children are likely to do in their overall reading performance by the end of the third grade.
- DIBELS identifies children who are at risk for reading difficulties before failure sets in, and determines appropriate instructional support.

What does it do?

- The DIBELS measures identify emerging literacy skills and risk status towards developing reading difficulties.

How does it work?

- Screening is administered to all students in the fall, mid-winter, and spring of each year, K–3.
- All measures are individually administered, and include scripted administration instructions.
- Each measure is timed for one minute, except for Initial Sounds Fluency.
- There are three or four short tasks at each grade level. Results help teachers identify skills, monitor progress, and intervene with students at risk.

What does it measure?

- **Letter Naming Fluency:** a student's knowledge of upper and lower-case letters arranged in a random order.
- **Initial Sound Fluency:** a student's ability to recognize and produce the initial sound in an orally presented word.
- **Phoneme Segmentation Fluency:** a student's ability to segment three and four phoneme words into their individual phonemes fluently.
- **Nonsense Word Fluency:** a student's knowledge of letter-sound correspondence and the student's ability to blend sounds into words.
- **Oral Reading and Retell Fluency:** a student's overall reading performance, and identifies students who may need additional instructional support in fluency and comprehension.
- **Word Use Fluency:** identifies students who may need additional instructional support with vocabulary strategies.

Aligning the DIBELS Screening Schedule with TREASURES

Kindergarten

TREASURES	DIBELS Measure	Start Smart/ Beginning	Unit 4/ Middle	Unit 9/ End
Phonemic Awareness	ISF	Goal: 8 Low Risk 8 or more Some Risk 4–7 At Risk below 4	Goal: 25–35 Established ≥ 25 Emerging 10–24 Deficit < 10	Move to PSF
	PSF		Goal: 18 correct phonemes Low Risk 18 Some Risk 7–17 At Risk < 7	Goal: 35 correct phonemes Established 35–45 Emerging 10–34 Deficit < 10
Letter Recognition	LNF	Goal: 8 correct letters Low Risk ≥ 8 Some Risk 2–7 At Risk < 2	Goal: 27 correct letters Low Risk ≥ 27 Some Risk 15–26 At Risk < 15	Goal: 40 correct letters Low Risk ≥ 40 Some Risk 29–39 At Risk < 29
Alphabetic Principle/ Phonics	NWF		Goal 13 correct letter sounds Low Risk ≥ 13 Some Risk 5–12 At Risk < 5	Goal 25 correct letter sounds Low Risk ≥ 25 Some Risk 15–24 At Risk < 15
Vocabulary	WUF	Low Risk > 20th percentile for your district or class At Risk ≤ 20th percentile for your district or class	Low Risk > 20th percentile for your district or class At Risk ≤ 20th percentile for your district or class	Low Risk > 20th percentile for your district or class At Risk ≤ 20th percentile for your district or class

Aligning the DIBELS Screening Schedule with TREASURES

First Grade

TREASURES	DIBELS Measure	Unit 1/ Beginning	Unit 3/ Middle	Unit 5/ End
Letter Recognition	LNF	Goal: 37 correct letters Low Risk ≥ 37 Some Risk 25–36 At Risk < 25		
Phonemic Awareness	PSF	Goal: 35 correct Phonemes Established 35–45 Emerging 10–34 Deficit < 10	Goal: 35 correct phonemes Established 35–45 Emerging 10–34 Deficit < 10	Goal: 35 correct phonemes Established 35–45 Emerging 10–34 Deficit < 10
Alphabetic Principle/ Phonics	NWF	Goal: 24 correct sounds Low Risk ≥ 24 Some Risk 13–23 At Risk 13	Goal: 50 correct sounds and 15 words recoded Established ≥ 50 ≥ 15 words recoded Emerging 30–49 < 15 words recoded Deficit < 30 < 15 words recoded	Goal: 50 correct sounds and 15 words recoded Established ≥ 50 ≥ 15 words recoded Emerging 30–49 < 15 words recoded Deficit < 30 < 15 words recoded
Fluency	ORF		Goal: 20 correct words per minute Low Risk > 20 Some Risk 8–19 At Risk ≤ 7	Goal: 40 correct words per minute Low Risk > 40 Some Risk 20–39 At Risk < 19
Comprehension	RTF		Goal: 50% of ORF score Low Risk > 25% At Risk ≤ 25%	Goal: 50% of ORF score Low Risk > 25% At Risk ≤ 25%
Vocabulary	WUF	Low Risk > 20th percentile At Risk ≤ 20th percentile	Low Risk > 20th percentile At Risk ≤ 20th percentile	Low Risk > 20th percentile At Risk ≤ 20th percentile

Aligning the DIBELS Screening Schedule with TREASURES

Second Grade

TREASURES	DIBELS Measure	Unit 1/ Beginning	Unit 3/ Middle	Unit 5/ End
Alphabetic Principle/ Phonics	NWF	Goal: 50 correct sounds and 15 words recoded Low Risk ≥ 50 ≥ 15 words recoded Some Risk 30–49 < 15 words recoded At Risk < 30 < 15 words recoded		
Fluency	ORF	Goal: 44 correct words per minute Low Risk > 44 Some Risk 26–43 At Risk ≤ 25	Goal: 68 correct words per minute Low Risk > 68 Some Risk 52–67 At Risk < 51	Goal: 90 correct words per minute Low Risk > 90 Some Risk 70–89 At Risk < 69
Comprehension	RTF	Goal: 50% of ORF score Low Risk > 25% of ORF Score At Risk ≤ 25% of ORF score	Goal: 50% of ORF score Low Risk > 25% of ORF Score At Risk ≤ 25% of ORF score	Goal: 50% of ORF score Low Risk > 25% of ORF Score At Risk ≤ 25% of ORF score
Vocabulary	WUF	Low Risk > 20th percentile for your district or class At Risk ≤ 20th percentile for your district or class	Low Risk > 20th percentile for your district or class At Risk ≤ 20th percentile for your district or class	Low Risk > 20th percentile for your district or class At Risk ≤ 20th percentile for your district or class

Aligning the DIBELS Screening Schedule with TREASURES

Third Grade

TREASURES	DIBELS Measure	Unit 1/ Beginning	Unit 3/ Middle	Unit 5/ End
Fluency	ORF	Goal: 77 correct words per minute Low Risk ≥ 77 Some Risk 53–76 At Risk ≤ 52	Goal: 92 correct words per minute Low Risk ≥ 92 Some Risk 67–91 At Risk ≤ 66	Goal: 110 correct words per minute Low Risk ≥ 110 Some Risk 80–109 At Risk ≤ 79
Comprehension	RTF	Goal: 50% of ORF score Low Risk > 25% of ORF Score At Risk ≤ 25% of ORF score	Goal: 50% of ORF score Low Risk > 25% of ORF Score At Risk ≤ 25% of ORF score	Goal: 50% of ORF score Low Risk > 25% of ORF Score At Risk ≤ 25% of ORF score
Vocabulary	WUF	Low Risk > 20th percentile for your district or class At Risk ≤ 20th percentile for your district or class	Low Risk > 20th percentile for your district or class At Risk ≤ 20th percentile for your district or class	Low Risk > 20th percentile for your district or class At Risk ≤ 20th percentile for your district or class

Using <u>TPRI</u> for Screening

What is the TPRI screening assessment?

- The Texas Primary Reading Inventory is a teacher-administered assessment that quickly identifies students who are NOT at risk of reading failure.
- It allows teachers to target their instruction and resources on those students who need further evaluation.
- It is a predictive assessment.

What does it do?

- The TPRI is designed to supplement and facilitate teacher judgment.
- It identifies students as developed or still developing literacy concepts.

How does it work?

- The screening test is a series of short (i.e. in three–five minutes), student-friendly tasks.
- The Kindergarten screening is administered in Mid-January and Mid-April.
- The Grade 1 screening is administered in Mid-September and Mid-April.
- The Grade 2 screening is administered in Mid-September.
- The Grade 3 screening is administered in Mid-September.

What do they measure?

- **Graphophonemic Knowledge:** the recognition of alphabet letters and the understanding of sound-symbol relationships.
- **Phonemic Awareness:** the ability to identify, think about, or manipulate the individual sounds in words.
- **Word Reading:** the correct identification of words. Students are identified as *Developed* or *Still Developing*.

How to Sequence the <u>TPRI</u> Kit

Step 1: Screening Section

- All students take the screening assessment.
- Allows you to identify students who are not likely to experience difficultly learning to read.
- Provides a way to focus additional resources on students who need more evaluation.

Step 2: Inventory Section

- Students who are *Still Developing* move on to the Inventory Section.
- Optional: Administer to all students for additional diagnostic information.

Step 3: Reading Accuracy, Fluency, and Comprehension
(Listening Comprehension in Grade K)

- Administer to all students.

Aligning the <u>TPRI</u> Screening Schedule with <u>TREASURES</u>

Kindergarten

Unit 4/Mid-Year: Phonemic Awareness, Graphophonemic Knowledge

Unit 9/End of Year: Phonemic Awareness, Graphophonemic Knowledge

First Grade

Unit 1/Beginning of Year: Phonemic Awareness, Graphophonemic Knowledge, and Word Reading

Unit 5/End of Year: Phonemic Awareness and Word Reading

Second Grade

Unit 1/Beginning of Year: Word Reading

Third Grade

Unit 1/Beginning of Year: Word Reading

Administering the TPRI Screening Assessment

1. Read the directions before beginning.

2. Begin with the practice items.

3. Administer the task to the student.

4. Be sure to pronounce the phonemes correctly.

5. Follow the Branching Rules.

6. Scoring criteria:
   Developed or *Still Developing*

7. Grade 2: Students who are identified as still developing on the TPRI screening at the beginning of grade 2 may be in need of intensive reading intervention.

8. Grade 3: The screening tasks should be simplified into one task. Administer all twenty items at one time. This makes it easier to administer and evaluate.

9. Third-grade students who do not read at least nineteen out of twenty words correctly on the combined tasks are at risk of falling below the 20th percentile on a standardized, end-of-the-year, reading test.

Diagnostic Options

Diagnostic Assessments

There are several diagnostic assessments you can use for identifying the strengths and weaknesses of your students. These can be used according to a schedule (see **TPRI** on **page 15** and **Fox in a Box** on **page 17**) or at any time during the year when in-depth information about a student is needed.

TPRI (Texas Primary Reading Inventory), K–3

For developing students, the Inventory portion of the **TPRI** allows teachers to gather specific diagnostic information. The Inventory section measures:

- Book and Print Awareness (K)
- Phonemic Awareness (K–1)
- Listening Comprehension (K–1)
- Graphophonemic Knowledge (K–3)
- Reading Accuracy (1–3)
- Reading Fluency (1–3)
- Reading Comprehension (1–3)

Fox in a Box, K–2

Fox in a Box provides benchmark levels for developmentally-appropriate activities. Systematic literacy activities diagnose students' skills in the following areas:

- Phonemic Awareness
- Phonics
- Reading
- Oral Expression
- Listening
- Writing

Informal Reading Inventory, 1–6

IRIs are silent and oral reading passages that are used to determine students' Independent, Instructional, and Frustrational reading levels. Students read successively more difficult, grade-level text, and answer vocabulary and comprehension questions.

Placement Tests, K–6

Placement Tests are used at the beginning of the year or any time you need additional diagnostic information. The Placement Tests specify the ranges of scores that help you decide whether students would benefit from on level (80%–90%), beyond level (over 90%), or approaching level (less than 80%) materials.

Using TPRI as a Diagnostic

What is the TPRI Inventory assessment?

- The Inventory is a diagnostic tool intended to guide instruction.
- The Inventory reveals students' strengths and weaknesses to help teachers plan differentiated classroom instruction.

What does it do?

- It gives teachers an opportunity to acquire more data to help match reading instruction with specific student needs.

How does it work?

- The Inventory is administered to all students who fail the screening section.
- It takes about twenty minutes to administer and materials are color coded.
- Concepts are considered *Developed* when students provide correct responses to the indicated number of items within a task. Teachers then proceed to the next task.
- If a student does not respond to the indicated number of items, the concept is considered *Still Developing*.
- At the beginning of the year, students are expected to score *Still Developing* on many of the Inventory tasks; they are expected to learn and develop the skills measured on the Inventory throughout the school year.

What does it measure?

- **Book and Print Awareness/Concepts of Print:** The ability to concentrate on the conventions and formats of print.
- **Phonemic Awareness:** The ability to attend to the sound structure of spoken language.
- **Graphophonemic Knowledge:** The ability to recognize letters and understand sound-spelling relationships.
- **Listening and Reading Comprehension:** Word lists help place students into the appropriate instructional reading level.
- **Reading Accuracy and Reading Fluency**

Inventory Branching Rules

- All tasks are arranged from easiest to most difficult.
- A basic task is the first or easiest one, and an advanced task is the last or hardest one.
- Begin with the easiest task and stay within the same portion of the Inventory as long as the student continues to score as *Developed*.
- If a student scores *Still Developing* on a task, stop and move the student to the next portion of the Inventory.

How to Prevent Student Frustration

- If the student is reading the entire passage at a Frustrational Level, stop and ask the student to read the previous passage instead.
- At Grades 1 and 2, the Frustrational Level is defined as the point when the student cannot read three or more words in the *first* sentence.
- In Grade 1, the teacher can read the story aloud and treat this as Listening Comprehension.
- In Grade 2, the teacher should administer the First Grade Word List before going back to a first-grade story.

Aligning the <u>TPRI</u> Inventory Schedule with <u>TREASURES</u>

Kindergarten

Unit 4/Middle of the Year and **Unit 9**/End of the Year:
Book and Print Awareness, Phonemic Awareness, Graphophonemic Knowledge, Reading/Listening Comprehension

First Grade

Unit 1/Beginning of Year, **Unit 3**/Middle of Year, and **Unit 5**/End of Year:
Phonemic Awareness, Graphophonemic Knowledge, Reading Accuracy, Fluency, and Reading/Listening Comprehension

Second and Third Grades

Unit 1/Beginning of Year, **Unit 3**/Middle of Year, and **Unit 5**/End of Year:
Graphophonemic Knowledge, Reading Accuracy, Fluency, and Reading/Listening Comprehension

Using <u>Fox in a Box</u> as a Diagnostic

What is the Fox in a Box diagnostic assessment?

- It is a balanced and comprehensive literacy assessment across grade levels.

What does it do?

- It helps determine which literacy skills require the most attention.
- It presents an ongoing record of growth from one grade to the next.

How does it work?

- The assessment is divided into four strands that provide information about a student's literacy skills.
- The assessment is administered twice during the school year; in early fall (October/November) and in early spring (March/April).

What does it measure?

Phonemic Awareness
- identify and generate rhymes
- clap out syllables
- isolate initial and final consonants
- blend phonemes to make words
- phoneme segmentation

Phonics
- recognize all uppercase letters and lowercase letters
- produce sounds of all letters
- write upper and lowercase letters
- decode phonetically regular and non-words

Reading and Oral Expression
- sight word recognition
- reading text comprehension
- concepts of print
- applying reading strategies
- speaking with effective vocabulary
- reading accuracy and reading fluency

Listening and Writing
- listening to a passage
- writing with comprehension about a passage

Using the Literacy Progress Record

The Literacy Progress Record (LPR) is a way to gather and record information about each child as they develop from Kindergarten to Grade 2.

- It allows you to record your observations, and the dates on which students master the benchmark activities.

- It shows progress across the year, across the grades, and in relation to the specific benchmarks.

- It allows you to share pertinent information with other teachers, parents, and school specialists.

- The activities and literacy strands must be administered in the correct order. The Overview of Activity Benchmarks, and the Flow Chart in the Teacher's Guide, help keep activities in the correct sequence.

- Write the child's score in the shaded box on the LPR following each activity. Fill in the date mastered for all scores that meet the benchmark.

- If the benchmark is not mastered, record the date that you administered the activity under Observations.

- When the student does master the activity, write the date on the inside front cover on the Record of Child's Progress.

- Be sure to record the dates when activities are mastered on both the activity itself and on the inside front cover.

- See the list of Activity Benchmarks on the inside front cover of the LPR.
    Level 1 Activities: Midyear Kindergarten
    Level 2 Activities: End of Kindergarten
    Level 3 Activities: Midyear Grade 1
    Level 4 Activities: End of Grade 1
    Level 5 Activities: Midyear Grade 2
    Level 6 Activities: End of Grade 2

Aligning the <u>Fox in a Box</u> Schedule with <u>TREASURES</u>

Kindergarten

Units 3–4/ Early fall (October/November)
Units 5–6/ Early spring (March/April)

First and Second Grades

Unit 2/ Early fall (October/November)
Unit 5/ Early spring (March/April)

Using the <u>Informal Reading Inventory</u> as a Diagnostic

What is an IRI diagnostic?

- The IRI is an individually-administered diagnostic that assesses a student's comprehension and reading accuracy in grades 1–6.

What does it do?

- The IRI determines a student's reading level. This level directly relates to the student's reading accuracy and comprehension of the passage.
- It assesses students' understanding of the stories with literal and interpretive comprehension questions.

How does it work?

- At each grade level, there are two fiction and two nonfiction reading passages.
- These passages alternate between oral reading and silent reading.
- There are three literal questions, one vocabulary question, and one interpretive question to assess the student's comprehension.
- On the teacher recording sheet, there is a table for each oral reading passage to help identify the student's reading level. This level is based on a combined score of comprehension points and word recognition errors. For each silent reading passage, the total number of comprehension points is used to determine a reading level.

What does it measure?

- The IRI measures oral and silent reading comprehension.
- It also measures reading word accuracy.

Using the Placement Tests

What are Placement Tests?

- Placement Tests are tests that help you do a preliminary evaluation of the abilities and instructional levels of your students.

What do they do?

- Placement Tests place students into appropriate grade levels.
- They also provide information to help place students into instructional groups.

How do they work?

- The Placement Tests are intended to be group administered except in Kindergarten, where the test is individually administered.
- The Placement Test should be administered at or near the beginning of the year, or when you receive new entrants.
- There is one Placement Test for each grade, and the results will help you place students in approaching, on level, and beyond level instructional groups.

What do they measure?

Kindergarten

- Concepts of Print
- Letter Recognition
- Phonics
- Word Recognition
- Listening Comprehension

First Grade

- Phonics
- Word Recognition
- Vocabulary
- Listening Comprehension

Second Grade

- Word Recognition
- Vocabulary
- Reading Comprehension

Third–Sixth Grades

- Vocabulary
- Reading Comprehension

Student Profiles: Using Screening and Diagnostic Assessments

Scenario #1: Fall, Grade 3

Test Score Results

The student's oral reading fluency score (the number of words read correctly per minute) was determined by having him read a third-grade passage from the Informal Reading Inventory (IRI).

- The score obtained was 59 words correct per minute (WCPM). This score is more than 12 WCPM below the 50th percentile score on the Oral Reading Fluency Norms chart for third grade in the fall (Hasbrouck & Tindal Oral Reading Fluency Norms 2005).
- The student's performance on the comprehension part of the IRI indicated that he could read and understand the passage at his instructional level.

How to Interpret Results

The teacher should expect that the student's fluency score reflects his instructional reading level.

Making Assessment Decisions

- A teacher might have the student read another third-grade level passage to determine if the fluency score was low due to some particular difficulty in the passage itself.
- If the score on the next passage is also more than 10 words below the 50th percentile, the student should receive additional fluency instruction.
- By winter, his fluency rate should change to a range of 82–92 WCPM on a new, unpracticed third-grade passage to be considered on track.

Scenario #2: Fall, Grade 4

ELL Student: native Spanish-speaker; student is becoming conversational in English; reading instruction provided entirely in English

Test Score Results

The teacher administered a one-minute fluency assessment using an unpracticed fourth-grade level passage.

- The student read 102 words in the passage and made 5 errors. This resulted in a score of 97 WCPM. This score is 4 words above the 50th percentile on the Hasbrouck & Tindal 2005 Oral Reading Fluency Norms chart.

How to Interpret Results

While this student seems to be making progress in learning to read in English—based on his daily performance—he is having a great deal of difficulty with comprehension.

- The teacher knows that her district uses oral reading fluency scores as an indicator of overall reading proficiency.
- This student's oral reading fluency score indicates he is on track in reading, but his daily performance indicates that he can decode but not comprehend.

Making Instructional Decisions

Oral reading fluency is one of the most powerful indicators of a student's overall progress in reading.

- However, even when using standardized fluency passages, a teacher should not consider a single score without looking at other information.
- A student who is learning to *speak* English, at the same time he or she is being taught to *read* in English, may make steady improvement in decoding skills but lag behind in acquiring vocabulary and comprehension skills.
- All assessments should be considered indicators of performance, and used within a broad context of information to guide professional decisions.

Scenario #3: Winter, Grade 5

Test Score Results

This student's reading level has been determined to be about 1.5 years below grade level.

- In January of fifth grade, she currently receives instruction using third-grade level materials.
- Her reading support (Tier 2/Title I) teacher has been monitoring her progress once a month, using the DIBELS progress monitoring assessment materials (DORF— DIBELS Oral Reading Fluency assessment) and fluency assessments.

Interpreting the Results

The teacher is concerned because the student's current oral reading fluency score showed that her performance may be declining.

- This month's score is eight words lower than the previous month's score.
- This puzzles the teacher because this student's daily performance has indicated that she is making steady progress in her reading.
- Now the teacher is wondering if she needs to make a significant change in this student's instructional program.

Making Instructional Decisions

Teachers need to understand that using fluency-based assessments to monitor students' progress is only one indicator of a student's progress.

- Even when using standardized and reliable passages, a teacher should not consider a single score without looking at other information.
- Most experts recommend that a teacher change a student's instructional program after three consecutive scores indicate a pattern of declining performance.
- It may be that the passage used for this month's assessment was particularly difficult for this student. The teacher may want to administer a different passage that is at the same level of difficulty.
- The teacher should also watch the student's daily performance. If two more assessments indicate no improvement, a plan to change the current instruction should be developed.

Scenario #4: Spring, Grade 6

Test Score Results

This student is considered a strong reader but is still involved in fluency practice activities such as rereading and graphing her fluency scores.

- She is getting frustrated because her fluency seems to be "stuck" around 200 WCPM. She cannot seem to raise her score higher, even though she is practicing and working hard.

Interpreting the Results

With all the current emphasis on reading fluency, some teachers and students are confused about how "fluent" they need to be.

- According to the Hasbrouck & Tindal 2005 Oral Reading Fluency Norms, a sixth-grade student who is reading 200 WCPM in the spring of sixth grade is slightly above the 90th percentile in fluency.
- She has probably reached a maximum level of fluency that is reasonable for her age level.

Making Instructional Decisions

The National Reading Panel (2000) identified five key component skills necessary for proficient reading: phonemic awareness, phonics/decoding, fluency, vocabulary, and comprehension. The first three skills in this list have a limit to the necessary levels of proficiency that teachers need to help students achieve.

- There comes a time when some of our students are "proficient enough" in phonemic awareness, phonics, and fluency.
- However, there will never be a point where any student has received "enough" instruction or practice in vocabulary and comprehension.
- This student (and her parents and teachers) should be reassured that her fluency skills appear to be excellent, and the teacher should redesign this student's instructional program to spend significantly less time practicing fluency and more time developing vocabulary, comprehension skills and strategies, and writing.

Teacher Notes

Oral Reading Fluency Screening Assessment for Grades 4–6

Overview

The Oral Reading Fluency Screening Assessment is designed to quickly identify children who may require diagnostic testing and additional instructional support to meet grade-level expectations. We recommend that the screening assessment be administered three times a year to measure students' fluency in the fall, winter, and spring.

The fluency passages that follow are to be used as benchmark assessments. Each passage has been leveled to reflect the fall, winter, and spring ranges of reading difficulty. Student performance is measured by having students do a timed reading of the selected passage. The number of Words Correct Per Minute (**WCPM**) is the student's oral fluency score.

As the student reads the passage, you should record errors such as omissions, substitutions, mispronunciations, word insertions, and hesitations of more than three seconds. Use the conventions that have been identified for marking word recognition errors on **page 69**. To calculate the number of words read correctly in one minute (**WCPM**), subtract the number of errors from the total number of words read. Refer to the **Curriculum-Based Oral Reading Fluency Norms** chart on **page 27** to obtain a percentile score for the fall, winter and spring to determine if a student is at risk. If a student's score falls more than 10 below the 25th percentile, consider evaluating the student for the **Macmillan/McGraw-Hill Reading Triumphs** Intervention Program. Administer the Individual Reading Inventory in this book as a diagnostic tool for those students who fall more than 10 below the 50th percentile.

Oral Reading Fluency Screener Grades 4–6

We recommend that a student read at least two passages before you evaluate the reading performance. There are nine fiction and nine nonfiction passages in the assessment. Each passage has one explicit and one implicit comprehension question which the student answers orally. The teacher records the student's response on the Fluency Record Sheet.

When evaluating a student's performance, it is critical to consider the student's oral response to the questions. If a student reads with perfect reading accuracy in the fall of fourth grade, but can't answer either of the comprehension questions, this student may need to read a passage at a lower grade level. It is essential to consider both the norms and the student's oral responses to determine if further testing and instructional intervention is necessary.

Administering Fluency Assessments and Using the Fluency Screening Record

Give the student a reading passage he or she has not seen before. Explain that you would like the student to read the passage out loud and then answer two questions about it. Then say: *When you are ready, you may begin.* Start your stopwatch when the student reads the first word.

1. Follow along on your copy as the student reads. Place a line through each word that is read incorrectly or omitted.

2. Place a check above each word that is read correctly.

3. If a student substitutes or mispronounces a word, put a line through the word and write the word said above it.

4. If the student does not correctly say the word within 3 seconds, say the word for the student and circle the word to mark it as incorrect. Self-corrections and repetitions are not considered errors.

5. At the end of each minute, stop your stopwatch and place a bracket (]) after the last word read by the student.

6. Have the student finish reading the passage.

7. Read the comprehension questions to the student. Have the student answer the comprehension questions orally.

8. Count each word you circled or put a line through. The total is the number of errors made. Subtract this number from the number of words read in one minute to arrive at the Oral Fluency Score, or **WCPM** score.

9. Use this formula to score Oral Reading Fluency:

$$\frac{\text{Total No. of Words Read} - \text{No. of Errors}}{\text{Total Number of Words Read}} \times 100$$

Curriculum-Based Oral Reading Fluency Norms

Use these norms to evaluate your student's oral reading fluency and determine whether diagnostic testing and intervention is necessary. Results are based on a one-minute timed sampling of a student's reading.

GRADE	PERCENTILE	FALL WCPM	WINTER WCPM	SPRING WCPM
4	90	145	166	180
	75	119	139	152
	50	94	112	123
	25	68	87	98
	10	45	61	72
	SD	40	41	43
5	90	166	182	194
	75	139	156	168
	50	110	127	139
	25	85	99	109
	10	61	74	83
	SD	45	44	45
6	90	177	195	204
	75	153	167	177
	50	127	140	150
	25	98	111	122
	10	68	82	93
	SD	42	45	44

A student's scores should fall within a range of ten WCPM above or below the score shown.

SD: Average standard deviation of scores

SOURCE Hasbrouck, J. & Tindal, G. (2005) norms for oral reading fluency. Eugene, OR: Behavioral Research & Teaching, University of Oregon.

Wild Visitors

Spring came early to the valley. One day, chilly winds rattled the trees, but then suddenly, the weather shifted. The meadows turned a lush green, and trees sprouted buds. Birdsong filled the air.

One Saturday at dawn, Rita woke up early. She found fishing tackle and an old sack of bread. Rainbow trout was in season this time of year. The area around Otter Creek was known for these small speckled fish. Rita hoped to catch a few to fry up for breakfast.

As she fished, she became more aware of the signs of the new season. Gazing at the stream, Rita felt calm and peaceful. She thought she was dreaming when a pair of bright eyes peered over the weeds by the stream.

It was a wild cat, just a kitten really. Rita realized it was wild from the long tufts of fur on its ears and the glint in its pale yellow eyes. Her heart sank. If her father knew there were wild cats on his land, he would have them destroyed. Farmers didn't want them around their barns. They ate birds and chickens. But this kitten was so cute, and it seemed hungry.

Just then, Rita felt a tug on her pole. A trout flipped and flopped at the end of the line. Quickly, she reeled it in and dropped it into her pail. That would make breakfast for one person. The little wild cat mewed loudly. The noise brought two more kittens to the banks of the stream. Rita tossed the fish she had caught to the kittens. She caught two more fish and threw those to them, too.

By late morning, the small wild family vanished back into the brush. "Did you catch anything?" her mother asked when she got home. "No," Rita replied. "It's still too cold for fishing."

1. What was Rita upset about?

2. How do wild cats survive?

Oral Reading Fluency Record Sheet

Name _____ Date _____

Oral Reading Accuracy: _____%   Circle: Fall Winter Spring

Oral Reading Fluency Score: _____ words correct per minute

Comprehension Questions Responses

#1 _____

#2 _____

Wild Visitors

Spring came early to the valley. One day, chilly winds rattled

11   the trees, but then suddenly, the weather shifted. The meadows

21   turned a lush green, and trees sprouted buds. Birdsong filled the air.

33   One Saturday at dawn, Rita woke up early. She found fishing tackle

45   and an old sack of bread. Rainbow trout was in season this time of year.

60   The area around Otter Creek was known for these small speckled fish.

72   Rita hoped to catch a few to fry up for breakfast.

83   As she fished, she became more aware of the signs of the new season.

97   Gazing at the stream, Rita felt calm and peaceful. She thought she was

110 dreaming when a pair of bright eyes peered over the weeds by the stream.

124 It was a wild cat, just a kitten really. Rita realized it was wild from the

140 long tufts of fur on its ears and the glint in its pale yellow eyes. Her heart

157 sank. If her father knew there were wild cats on his land, he would have

172 them destroyed. Farmers didn't want them around their barns. They ate

183 birds and chickens. But this kitten was so cute, and it seemed hungry.

196 Just then, Rita felt a tug on her pole. A trout flipped and flopped at the

212 end of the line. Quickly, she reeled it in and dropped it into her pail. That

228 would make breakfast for one person. The little wild cat mewed loudly.

240 The noise brought two more kittens to the banks of the stream. Rita tossed

254 the fish she had caught to the kittens. She caught two more fish and threw

269 those to them, too.

273 By late morning, the small wild family vanished back into the brush.

285 "Did you catch anything?" her mother asked when she got home.

296 "No," Rita replied. "It's still too cold for fishing." **305**

Number of words read: _____   Number of errors made: _____

The Panama Canal

The Panama Canal exists because it was a dream of Theodore Roosevelt's. The 26th American President wanted to link our two coasts. He hoped to build a canal between the Atlantic and the Pacific Oceans. There were sound reasons to build a canal. Ships would not have to sail all the way around Cape Horn. That was a long and dangerous trip. Goods could be shipped much more quickly.

But could the canal be built? Others had tried and failed. First, they had to decide where to build. The Isthmus of Panama was chosen. This narrow neck of land joined North and South America. The canal could cut through this piece of land.

The United States government paid the people of Panama ten million dollars. That gave the U.S. the right to dig the canal. At first, things went badly. Many workers became very sick. President Roosevelt brought in John Stevens, a skilled engineer. Stevens brought doctors to Panama. The doctors learned that mosquitoes carried diseases. They found ways to get rid of the bugs. This helped the workers stay well and fit.

Stevens also had a new plan. Instead of digging to sea level, he told workers to try another way. They would build a "lake and lock" canal. This would help raise the water level so that ships could pass easily over the rocky areas. The canal workers began building dams. The work was very hard. Stevens gave up. Then Thomas Goethals took over. There was still more grueling work to do.

It took ten years to finish the work. Finally, on August 13, 1914, the Panama Canal was opened. Roosevelt's dream had come true.

1. What kind of person was Theodore Roosevelt?
2. How did John Stevens change the plan for the canal?

Oral Reading Fluency Record Sheet

Name _____ Date _____

Oral Reading Accuracy: _____%   Circle: Fall   Winter   Spring

Oral Reading Fluency Score: _____ words correct per minute

Comprehension Questions Responses

#1 _____

#2 _____

The Panama Canal

      The Panama Canal exists because it was a dream of Theodore

11   Roosevelt's. The 26th American President wanted to link our two coasts. He

23   hoped to build a canal between the Atlantic and the Pacific Oceans. There

36   were sound reasons to build a canal. Ships would not have to sail all the

51   way around Cape Horn. That was a long and dangerous trip. Goods could

64   be shipped much more quickly.

69   But could the canal be built? Others had tried and failed. First, they

82   had to decide where to build. The Isthmus of Panama was chosen. This

95   narrow neck of land joined North and South America. The canal could cut

108   through this piece of land.

113   The United States government paid the people of Panama ten million

124   dollars. That gave the U.S. the right to dig the canal. At first, things went

139   badly. Many workers became very sick. President Roosevelt brought in

149   John Stevens, a skilled engineer. Stevens brought doctors to Panama. The

160   doctors learned that mosquitoes carried diseases. They found ways to get

171   rid of the bugs. This helped the workers stay well and fit.

183   Stevens also had a new plan. Instead of digging to sea level, he told

197   workers to try another way. They would build a "lake and lock" canal. This

211   would help raise the water level so that ships could pass easily over the

225   rocky areas. The canal workers began building dams. The work was very

237   hard. Stevens gave up. Then Thomas Goethals took over. There was still

249   more grueling work to do.

254   It took ten years to finish the work. Finally, on August 13, 1914, the

268   Panama Canal was opened. Roosevelt's dream had come true. **277**

Number of words read: _____   Number of errors made: _____

The Carp Pond

Kira awoke with the feeling that something special was going to happen. It was the first real day of her visit to Grandmother Lee. The train had brought her to the station late last evening. In the moonless night, Kira had not been able to admire Grandmother's famous gardens or the fishpond. Now, though, she would go and explore.

The sun shone warm and bright on the speckled grass. Kira went down the steps, and there was the fishpond, a blue jewel sparkling in the early summer light.

Some large golden fish glittered in the pool among the lily pads. Grandmother had told her these fish were called carp. One shimmied up to her toe and started to nibble, and Kira laughed out loud.

"Sorry to disappoint you, Mr. Fish!" she giggled.

The fish swam back and seemed to study her, and then it opened its jaws and thrust out something round and silvery.

It was a delicate silver ring. Amazingly, it just fit her fourth finger. "Maybe this is a magic wishing ring?" Kira whispered with uncertainty. So she decided to try it out. "I wish for a really huge breakfast," she said.

Someone was crossing the lawn. It was Grandmother's assistant John, who managed the cooking and chores. He was bearing a tray in his hands. "I believe you scooted out without your breakfast!" he called out.

"Oh—thanks!" Kira said, with surprise at the speed with which the ring had granted her request. When she had finished eating, Kira tried again. "I wish for a horse to ride."

John returned leading a tan pony with a white mane. This was eerie. Kira slid the ring off her finger and tossed it back into the pond.

© Macmillan/McGraw-Hill

1. How did Kira get the silver ring?
2. Why did Kira throw the ring back into the pond?

Oral Reading Fluency Record Sheet

Name _____ Date _____

Oral Reading Accuracy: _____%   Circle: Fall   Winter   Spring
Oral Reading Fluency Score: _____ words correct per minute
Comprehension Questions Responses
#1 _____
#2 _____

The Carp Pond

Kira awoke with the feeling that something special was going to happen.

12   It was the first real day of her visit to Grandmother Lee. The train had

27   brought her to the station late last evening. In the moonless night, Kira had

41   not been able to admire Grandmother's famous gardens or the fishpond.

52   Now, though, she would go and explore.

59   The sun shone warm and bright on the speckled grass. Kira went down

72   the steps, and there was the fishpond, a blue jewel sparkling in the early

86   summer light.

88   Some large golden fish glittered in the pool among the lily pads.

100   Grandmother had told her these fish were called carp. One shimmied up

112   to her toe and started to nibble, and Kira laughed out loud.

124   "Sorry to disappoint you, Mr. Fish!" she giggled.

132   The fish swam back and seemed to study her, and then it opened its

146   jaws and thrust out something round and silvery.

154   It was a delicate silver ring. Amazingly, it just fit her fourth finger.

167   "Maybe this is a magic wishing ring?" Kira whispered with uncertainty. So

178   she decided to try it out. "I wish for a really huge breakfast," she said.

193   Someone was crossing the lawn. It was Grandmother's assistant John,

203   who managed the cooking and chores. He was bearing a tray in his hands.

217   "I believe you scooted out without your breakfast!" he called out.

228   "Oh—thanks!" Kira said, with surprise at the speed with which the ring

241   had granted her request. When she had finished eating, Kira tried again.

253   "I wish for a horse to ride."

260   John returned leading a tan pony with a white mane. This was eerie.

273   Kira slid the ring off her finger and tossed it back into the pond. **287**

Number of words read: _____   Number of errors made: _____

© Macmillan/McGraw-Hill

Alice Walker, Writer

The story of Alice Walker would encourage anyone—especially a budding writer. Walker was born in 1944 in Eatonton, Georgia. Her parents, Willie Lee and Minnie, were sharecroppers. That meant they farmed land that was owned by someone else. Their lives were hard. The Walkers had eight children to feed and to clothe. But this did not put an end to fun.

When Alice was eight, her eye was injured in a game. A scar formed. This scar made Alice feel bad about herself. She began reading and writing poetry in order to deal with her feelings. Her years of loneliness would make her a great writer.

When she was fourteen, an older brother wanted to help Alice. He took her to a hospital where the scar on her eye was removed. Alice began to feel better about the way she looked. She welcomed a second chance to make friends. In fact, she made so many friends that she was voted queen of her senior prom.

While Alice was in college in the North, she gave some of her poems to her teacher, a famous poet. Her teacher eagerly showed Alice's poems to an editor. Three years later, Alice published her first book, *Once*.

After college, Alice went back to the South. She helped other African Americans to vote and also worked for Head Start, a program for children. Walker was still writing, and life gave her plenty of material to write about. In 1967, Walker married. She and her husband wanted things to change in the South. They worked hard and faced real dangers. But Alice kept writing. She has won many awards for her work.

© Macmillan/McGraw-Hill

1. Why did Alice begin to feel bad about herself?
2. What is the main idea of the story?

Oral Reading Fluency Record Sheet

Name _____   Date _____

Oral Reading Accuracy: _____%   Circle: Fall   Winter   Spring
Oral Reading Fluency Score: _____ words correct per minute
Comprehension Questions Responses
#1 _____
#2 _____

Alice Walker, Writer

The story of Alice Walker would encourage anyone—especially a

10   budding writer. Walker was born in 1944 in Eatonton, Georgia. Her

21   parents, Willie Lee and Minnie, were sharecroppers. That meant they

31   farmed land that was owned by someone else. Their lives were hard. The

44   Walkers had eight children to feed and to clothe. But this did not put an

59   end to fun.

62   When Alice was eight, her eye was injured in a game. A scar formed.

76   This scar made Alice feel bad about herself. She began reading and

88   writing poetry in order to deal with her feelings. Her years of loneliness

101 would make her a great writer.

107 When she was fourteen, an older brother wanted to help Alice. He took

120 her to a hospital where the scar on her eye was removed. Alice began to

137 feel better about the way she looked. She welcomed a second chance to

150 make friends. In fact, she made so many friends that she was voted queen

164 of her senior prom.

168 While Alice was in college in the North, she gave some of her poems

182 to her teacher, a famous poet. Her teacher eagerly showed Alice's poems

194 to an editor. Three years later, Alice published her first book, *Once*.

206 After college, Alice went back to the South. She helped other African

218 Americans to vote and also worked for Head Start, a program for children.

231 Walker was still writing, and life gave her plenty of material to write

244 about. In 1967, Walker married. She and her husband wanted things to

256 change in the South. They worked hard and faced real dangers. But Alice

269 kept writing. She has won many awards for her work. **279**

Number of words read: _____   Number of errors made: _____

A Boy Called Amos

When Amos Gray first arrived at school, everyone stared at him. He wore clothing that was too big for his thin frame. His coarse brown hair stuck out in strange places. He brought his own lunch—a tin of sardines and a roll. This all seemed very odd to the others. The teacher wanted to know why Amos had started school in the middle of the term. The principal asked to meet with Amos's parents. Amos replied that his mother was ill at the moment. A visit would have to wait. Amos smiled as he explained these things to the principal.

Amit Singh had not attended this school very long. His family originally came from India and they had moved here only a year ago. So Amit too felt that he was a stranger of sorts. Amos flashed a smile at people when they spoke or behaved foolishly. This convinced Amit that Amos Gray had a strong and interesting personality. Amit was sure he and the newcomer could become friends.

So one day, Amit secretly followed Amos home across a muddy field and down a winding dirt road. Amos finally turned off the road and approached an abandoned bus. The vehicle looked in need of some serious repairs. Dark cloths were draped over some of its windows. Amit hesitated. After a moment, he knocked on the bus door.

"You found me, I see," Amos uttered calmly. His way of talking made Amit feel comfortable right away.

"Would you like to play a game?" Amos invited him in.

The shabby bus looked well-swept. And Amos' mother smiled sweetly at them both. Amos and Amit were about to become friends.

© Macmillan/McGraw-Hill

1. In what way were Amos and Amit alike?

2. How were they different?

Oral Reading Fluency Record Sheet

Name _____ Date _____

Oral Reading Accuracy: _____%   Circle: Fall Winter Spring

Oral Reading Fluency Score: _____ words correct per minute

Comprehension Questions Responses

#1 _____

#2 _____

A Boy Called Amos

When Amos Gray first arrived at school, everyone stared at him. He

12   wore clothing that was too big for his thin frame. His coarse brown hair

26   stuck out in strange places. He brought his own lunch—a tin of sardines

40   and a roll. This all seemed very odd to the others. The teacher wanted to

55   know why Amos had started school in the middle of the term. The

68   principal asked to meet with Amos's parents. Amos replied that his

79   mother was ill at the moment. A visit would have to wait. Amos smiled

93   as he explained these things to the principal.

101   Amit Singh had not attended this school very long. His family originally

113   came from India and they had moved here only a year ago. So Amit too felt

129   that he was a stranger of sorts. Amos flashed a smile at people when

143   they spoke or behaved foolishly. This convinced Amit that Amos Gray

154   had a strong and interesting personality. Amit was sure he and the

166   newcomer could become friends.

170   So one day, Amit secretly followed Amos home across a muddy field

182   and down a winding dirt road. Amos finally turned off the road and

195   approached an abandoned bus. The vehicle looked in need of some serious

207   repairs. Dark cloths were draped over some of its windows. Amit

218   hesitated. After a moment, he knocked on the bus door.

228   "You found me, I see," Amos uttered calmly. His way of talking made

241   Amit feel comfortable right away.

246   "Would you like to play a game?" Amos invited him in.

257   The shabby bus looked well-swept. And Amos' mother smiled sweetly

268   at them both. Amos and Amit were about to become friends. **279**

Number of words read: _____   Number of errors made: _____

Ebu Gogo: Hobbit or Not?

Many people have enjoyed the movies about a tiny race of people called hobbits. These movies, The Lord of the Rings, were based on books by the author J.R.R. Tolkien. The author had a lively imagination. However, there may be more to the story.

In 2004, several skeletons were dug up on the island of Flores, in Indonesia. Some call Flores a "Lost World." Many ancient animal species lived there. A small species of human beings even settled there, too.

Scientists who discovered the remains of these people call them "hobbits." Just like Tolkien's make-believe hobbits, these early people were very small. Their skulls were tiny, and they probably had hairy feet.

But should we really call these people "hobbits?" Scientists say they would have looked different from Tolkien's storybook beings. They are studying the skulls and bones found in the caves.

The real facts are as interesting as a fantasy tale. About 12,000 years ago, a volcano erupted on Flores. Most of the animals would have been killed. Tests have shown that the little skeletons date back some 18,000 years. Yet, on Flores, stories are told about the small people. They are called "Ebu Gogo." Nobody knows how long they lived. But there are clues about *how* they lived.

Ebu Gogo made their homes in caves. They made stone tools. They also probably built boats. Yet, they were not as "smart" as later peoples. Their brains were as small as grapefruits. Ebu Gogo probably died out long ago. Some believe they survive on other islands in Indonesia. Someday we may know their whole story.

© Macmillan/McGraw-Hill

1. Where did Ebu Gogo live?
2. What is the author's viewpoint about Ebu Gogo?

Oral Reading Fluency Record Sheet

Name _____ Date _____

Oral Reading Accuracy: _____%　　　　Circle:　Fall　Winter　Spring

Oral Reading Fluency Score: _____ words correct per minute

Comprehension Questions Responses

#1 _____

#2 _____

Ebu Gogo: Hobbit or Not?

　　　　Many people have enjoyed the movies about a tiny race of people

12　　called hobbits. These movies, The Lord of the Rings, were based on books

25　　by the author J.R.R. Tolkien. The author had a lively imagination.

36　　However, there may be more to the story.

44　　　　In 2004, several skeletons were dug up on the island of Flores, in

57　　Indonesia. Some call Flores a "Lost World." Many ancient animal species

68　　lived there. A small species of human being even settled there, too.

80　　　　Scientists who discovered the remains of these people call them

90　　"hobbits." Just like Tolkien's make-believe hobbits, these early people

100　　were very small. Their skulls were tiny, and they probably had hairy feet.

113　　　　But should we really call these people "hobbits?" Scientists say they

124　　would have looked different from Tolkien's storybook beings. They are

134　　studying the skulls and bones found in the caves.

143　　　　The real facts are as interesting as a fantasy tale. About 12,000 years

156　　ago, a volcano erupted on Flores. Most of the animals would have been

169　　killed. Tests have shown that the little skeletons date back some 18,000

181　　years. Yet, on Flores, stories are told about the small people. They are

194　　called "Ebu Gogo." Nobody knows how long they lived. But there are

206　　clues about how they lived.

211　　　　Ebu Gogo made their homes in caves. They made stone tools. They

223　　also probably built boats. Yet, they were not as "smart" as later peoples.

236　　Their brains were as small as grapefruits. Ebu Gogo probably died out

248　　long ago. Some believe they survive on other islands in Indonesia.

259　　Someday we may know their whole story.　**266**

Number of words read: _____　　Number of errors made: _____

Spooky Night

Ethan tossed uneasily on his pillow. For the first time ever, he was alone in the house at night. His parents had gone to a party and were not returning until midnight. Ethan had assured his mother that he was not afraid. Then the storm came, and Ethan began to regret his earlier decision.

Ethan had watched his favorite television program and prepared a snack. After brushing his teeth, he had read a chapter of an adventure story. But thunder pounded at the roof, and a series of strange noises from the backyard made it impossible to rest. What if there was a burglar out there, lurking around until the time was ripe? True, he had seen his father turn on the alarm system, but everyone knew clever thieves could disable complicated alarms.

Ethan panicked when he heard a muffled crash from beyond his open window. He hurriedly found his baseball bat and a flashlight, then tiptoed downstairs without switching on the lights. He was planning to launch a silent attack on the thief. Ethan padded through the hallway to the front door. He could feel his blood rushing up to his ears. He had never felt so terrified. Ethan yanked open the door and trained the flashlight on the lawn.

Rain spattered from the gutters of the house. The trees cast long shadows, and the blackness hid everything. Ethan froze when he heard a thud.

Suddenly a bulky figure loomed in the driveway. Ethan screamed.

"Ethan! What's wrong?" his father's voice called.

"N-nothing," Ethan stammered feebly.

"Then come help us move these branches out of the driveway."

"Sure, Dad!" Ethan said, delighted to do the chore.

1. What is the theme of the story?
2. What caused the strange sounds Ethan heard?

Oral Reading Fluency Record Sheet

Name _____ Date _____

Oral Reading Accuracy: _____%   Circle: Fall   Winter   Spring
Oral Reading Fluency Score: _____ words correct per minute
Comprehension Questions Responses
#1 _____
#2 _____

Spooky Night

Ethan tossed uneasily on his pillow. For the first time ever, he was alone

14 in the house at night. His parents had gone to a party and were not returning

30 until midnight. Ethan had assured his mother that he was not afraid. Then the

44 storm came, and Ethan began to regret his earlier decision.

55 Ethan had watched his favorite television program and prepared a snack.

66 After brushing his teeth, he had read a chapter of an adventure story. But

80 thunder pounded at the roof, and a series of strange noises from the backyard

94 made it impossible to rest. What if there was a burglar out there, lurking

108 around until the time was ripe? True, he had seen his father turn on the alarm

124 system, but everyone knew clever thieves could disable complicated alarms.

134 Ethan panicked when he heard a muffled crash from beyond his open

146 window. He hurriedly found his baseball bat and a flashlight, then tiptoed

158 downstairs without switching on the lights. He was planning to launch a

170 silent attack on the thief. Ethan padded through the hallway to the front door.

184 He could feel his blood rushing up to his ears. He had never felt so terrified.

200 Ethan yanked open the door and trained the flashlight on the lawn.

212 Rain spattered from the gutters of the house. The trees cast long shadows

225 and the blackness hid everything. Ethan froze when he heard a thud.

237 Suddenly a bulky figure loomed in the driveway. Ethan screamed.

247 "Ethan! What's wrong?" his father's voice called.

254 "N-nothing," Ethan stammered feebly.

258 "Then come help us move these branches out of the driveway."

270 "Sure, Dad!" Ethan said, delighted to do the chore. **279**

Number of words read: _____   Number of errors made: _____

Tsunamis

Natural disasters are nothing new on our planet. Floods, fires, storms, and earthquakes strike every year. People have found ways to deal with some of these disasters. Yet, there are forces stronger than any human being.

A case in point is the tsunami, or tidal wave. A mighty tsunami swept through the Indian Ocean on December 26, 2004. It killed thousands of people. Tsunamis are powerful ocean waves. They are set in motion by earthquakes, landslides, or volcanic eruptions. A tsunami can reach thirty meters in height. It can sweep away houses, trees, and people in a few seconds.

How do tsunamis form? The answer lies beneath the waves. There are places under the sea where the biggest tsunamis are most likely to develop. There the ground is uplifted and down-dropped. A quake forces the water column up over the fault. Giant waves move toward shore. They start to slow down as they travel. Yet, the tsunami still has great energy. This energy causes the water to rise up as it nears a coast.

Lesser tsunamis may weaken before hitting a beach. Then only a small area of land is damaged. Such tsunamis probably happen quite often. Still, they are dangerous. They cause flooding and strip sand from beaches. They can wreck beach houses and take lives.

Sometimes a tsunami can be predicted. Warning systems operate in the Pacific, where tsunamis usually occur. Scientists try to figure out where underwater quakes might take place. News shows on radio and television warn people in the area. Most people will move quickly from their homes to safer land. A warning ahead of time can save many lives.

1. What happens underwater as a tsunami develops?
2. Give a short summary of this article.

Oral Reading Fluency Record Sheet

Name _____   Date _____

Oral Reading Accuracy: _____%   Circle: Fall   Winter   Spring
Oral Reading Fluency Score: _____ words correct per minute
Comprehension Questions Responses
#1 _____
#2 _____

Tsunamis

Natural disasters are nothing new on our planet. Floods, fires, storms, and

14 earthquakes strike every year. People have found ways to deal with some of

32 these disasters. Yet, there are forces stronger than any human being.

36 A case in point is the tsunami, or tidal wave. A mighty tsunami swept

54 through the Indian Ocean on December 26, 2004. It killed thousands of

71 people. Tsunamis are powerful ocean waves. They are set in motion by

83 earthquakes, landslides, or volcanic eruptions. A tsunami can reach thirty

93 meters in height. It can sweep away houses, trees, and people in a

106 few seconds.

108 How do tsunamis form? The answer lies beneath the waves. There are

120 places under the sea where the biggest tsunamis are most likely to develop.

133 There the ground is uplifted and down-dropped. A quake forces the water

146 column up over the fault. Giant waves move toward shore. They start to slow

160 down as they travel. Yet, the tsunami still has great energy. This energy

173 causes the water to rise up as it nears a coast.

184 Lesser tsunamis may weaken before hitting a beach. Then only a small

196 area of land is damaged. Such tsunamis probably happen quite often. Still,

208 they are dangerous. They cause flooding and strip sand from beaches. They

220 can wreck beach houses and take lives.

227 Sometimes a tsunami can be predicted. Warning systems operate in the

238 Pacific, where tsunamis usually occur. Scientists try to figure out where

249 underwater quakes might take place. News shows on radio and television

260 warn people in the area. Most people will move quickly from their homes to

274 safer land. A warning ahead of time can save many lives. **285**

Number of words read: _____   Number of errors made: _____

A House Divided

It was a warm June day in Springfield, Illinois. Sallie and her little sister Lou wriggled on the hard bench. Their father had brought them here to the Capitol building to hear somebody give a speech.

"Shh!" Father hissed at them. "Mr. Lincoln will address the Senate now."

A tall, lanky man with a long, solemn face stood before the audience. This was Mr. Abraham Lincoln, the Republican nominee for the Senate. Sallie knew that Father and Mother admired this man. He was against slavery and was known to have strong views about the Dred Scott case.

Mr. Lincoln spoke for a while. Lou grew restless, and Father told her to hush. Sallie wished Lou had stayed home with Mother and the baby. Sometimes, she was a real pest. Sallie leaned forward to hear the speaker's words. "A house divided against itself cannot stand," Mr. Lincoln rumbled.

Mr. Lincoln spoke for quite a while. He believed that if slavery were permitted to spread across the country, the nation would be in danger. Father nodded several times. He seemed to have forgotten all about the two girls.

After the speech, Father stopped to chat with a small group of men.

"Mr. Douglas would allow each territory to make its own legislation about slavery," a man declared.

"We cannot leave the issue of slavery to the whims of the territories. We must adopt a position our entire nation will embrace," Father said.

As the girls followed Father down the dusty main street, Sallie tried out the words silently: "A house divided against itself cannot stand." She took Lou's hand and helped her over the rutted road.

1. What did Mr. Lincoln believe about slavery?

2. What did Sallie learn from Mr. Lincoln's speech?

Oral Reading Fluency Record Sheet

Name _____ Date _____

Oral Reading Accuracy: _____%　　　　Circle: Fall Winter Spring
Oral Reading Fluency Score: _____ words correct per minute
Comprehension Questions Responses
#1 _____
#2 _____

A House Divided

　　　　It was a warm June day in Springfield, Illinois. Sallie and her little sister

14　Lou wriggled on the hard bench. Their father had brought them here to the

28　Capitol building to hear somebody give a speech.

36　　　　"Shh!" Father hissed at them. "Mr. Lincoln will address the Senate now."

48　　　　A tall, lanky man with a long, solemn face stood before the audience.

61　This was Mr. Abraham Lincoln, the Republican nominee for the Senate.

72　Sallie knew that Father and Mother admired this man. He was against

85　slavery and was known to have strong views about the Dred Scott case.

99　　　　Mr. Lincoln spoke for a while. Lou grew restless, and Father told her to

113　hush. Sallie wished Lou had stayed home with Mother and the baby.

125　Sometimes, she was a real pest. Sallie leaned forward to hear the speaker's

138　words. "A house divided against itself cannot stand," Mr. Lincoln rumbled.

149　　　　Mr. Lincoln spoke for quite a while. He believed that if slavery were

162　permitted to spread across the country, the nation would be in danger. Father

175　nodded several times. He seemed to have forgotten all about the two girls.

188　　　　After the speech, Father stopped to chat with a small group of men.

201　　　　"Mr. Douglas would allow each territory to make its own legislation

212　about slavery," a man declared.

217　　　　"We cannot leave the issue of slavery to the whims of the territories. We

231　must adopt a position our entire nation will embrace," Father said.

242　　　　As the girls followed Father down the dusty main street, Sallie tried out

255　the words silently: "A house divided against itself cannot stand." She took

267　Lou's hand and helped her over the rutted road. **276**

Number of words read: _____　Number of errors made: _____

Martha Graham: A Dance Legend

If you have ever watched a performance of modern dance, you already know something about Martha Graham. Perhaps you have seen photographs of her. The woman who championed freedom in dance did not look like a ballerina. She did not don the painful toe shoes worn for ballet. She did not try to look like a vision of other-worldly beauty. Instead, she danced in bare feet. She made her face reveal all the emotions known to human beings.

Martha Graham was born in Pennsylvania in 1894. Her family moved to California, where Graham studied acting. At the age of seventeen, Martha saw a performance by Ruth St. Denis, a dancer inspired by ancient beliefs and practices. A few years later, Graham joined St. Denis's dance troupe. She was already old to take up dancing. But this did not stop Martha Graham. For seven years, she worked with St. Denis.

She later moved to New York City, where she started her own dance troupe. Graham took up different jobs to support her art. She worked as a model, and also taught acting classes. Gradually, she created a style all her own.

Graham became known for the system of breath control she developed. Her dancers learned to tense their bodies, then leap into motion. It was not a fluid style. Some even called it ugly. But her style reflected primitive movements which were suited to the themes she liked.

Martha Graham made a strong impression on those who saw her work. She was forceful and unforgettable. She brought drama to the dance. Her work was startling: sometimes, it even appeared to be violent. Every movement she made told a story. And the story became the dance.

1. Who first inspired Martha Graham to learn modern dance?

2. Why do you think the author wrote this article?

Oral Reading Fluency Record Sheet

Name _____ Date _____

Oral Reading Accuracy: _____%   Circle: Fall   Winter   Spring

Oral Reading Fluency Score: _____ words correct per minute

Comprehension Questions Responses

#1 _____

#2 _____

Martha Graham: A Dance Legend

      If you have ever watched a performance of modern dance, you already

12   know something about Martha Graham. Perhaps you have seen photographs

22   of her. The woman who championed freedom in dance did not look like a

36   ballerina. She did not don the painful toe shoes worn for ballet. She did not

51   try to look like a vision of other-worldly beauty. Instead, she danced in bare

66   feet. She made her face reveal all the emotions known to human beings.

79   Martha Graham was born in Pennsylvania in 1894. Her family moved to

92   California, where Graham studied acting. At the age of seventeen, Martha

103 saw a performance by Ruth St. Denis, a dancer inspired by ancient beliefs

116 and practices. A few years later, Graham joined St. Denis's dance troupe.

128 She was already old to take up dancing. But this did not stop Martha

142 Graham. For seven years, she worked with St. Denis.

151   She later moved to New York City, where she started her own dance troupe.

165 Graham took up different jobs to support her art. She worked as a model, and

181 also taught acting classes. Gradually, she created a style all her own.

193   Graham became known for the system of breath control she developed.

204 Her dancers learned to tense their bodies, then leap into motion. It was not

218 a fluid style. Some even called it ugly. But her style reflected primitive

231 movements which were suited to the themes she liked.

240   Martha Graham made a strong impression on those who saw her work.

252 She was forceful and unforgettable. She brought drama to the dance. Her

264 work was startling: sometimes, it even appeared to be violent. Every

275 movement she made told a story. And the story became the dance. **287**

Number of words read: _____   Number of errors made: _____

Possession

Terry and her cousin Alec were celebrating the first crisp autumn Saturday by having a picnic in Old Joseph's Meadow. Old Joseph, who was long departed, could not have objected to their merry voices or the worn blanket they spread across the lush grass.

"So who owns the title to this land, anyway?" Terry wondered.

"I don't know whether it's still private property," Alec replied. "The original family who possessed the land left the region a decade ago."

After lunch, they strolled around the meadow. Terry amused herself by doing cartwheels across the grass. On the fourth cartwheel, she collapsed.

"Ouch—I caught my foot on something. There's something under the grass here." Terry sat up and began to scrape at the ground with her fingers. Alec took a couple of spoons from the picnic basket, and they began digging.

Alec eventually paused to examine a small shard of pottery that his spoon had unearthed. His voice grew excited as he inspected the minute fragment. "This appears to be ancient—and remember, we're not too far from the old mounds. Centuries ago, Native Americans conducted ceremonies, like burials. They buried their leaders along with their cherished possessions."

After several hours, they had uncovered a few ceramic fragments.

"What will we do with our treasures?" Terry wondered. "Should we release this collection to the authorities?"

"I think we should bury it all again," Alec replied thoughtfully. "Nobody can claim these things now. We'll leave them in the earth, where they were intended to remain."

1. What is the main idea of the story?

2. Where did the fragments of pottery probably come from?

Oral Reading Fluency Record Sheet

Name _____ Date _____

Oral Reading Accuracy: _____%   Circle: Fall   Winter   Spring

Oral Reading Fluency Score: _____ words correct per minute

Comprehension Questions Responses

#1 _____

#2 _____

Possession

Terry and her cousin Alec were celebrating the first crisp autumn

11   Saturday by having a picnic in Old Joseph's Meadow. Old Joseph, who was

24   long departed, could not have objected to their merry voices or the worn

37   blanket they spread across the lush grass.

44   "So who owns the title to this land, anyway?" Terry wondered.

55   "I don't know whether it's still private property," Alec replied. "The

66   original family who possessed the land left the region a decade ago."

78   After lunch, they strolled around the meadow. Terry amused herself by

89   doing cartwheels across the grass. On the fourth cartwheel, she collapsed.

100   "Ouch—I caught my foot on something. There's something under the

111   grass here." Terry sat up and began to scrape at the ground with her fingers.

126   Alec took a couple of spoons from the picnic basket, and they began digging.

140   Alec eventually paused to examine a small shard of pottery that his spoon

153   had unearthed. His voice grew excited as he inspected the minute fragment.

165   "This appears to be ancient—and remember, we're not too far from the old

179   mounds. Centuries ago, Native Americans conducted ceremonies, like

187   burials. They buried their leaders along with their cherished possessions."

197   After several hours, they had uncovered a few ceramic fragments.

207   "What will we do with our treasures?" Terry wondered. "Should we

218   release this collection to the authorities?"

224   "I think we should bury it all again," Alec replied thoughtfully. "Nobody

236   can claim these things now. We'll leave them in the earth, where they were

250   intended to remain." **253**

Number of words read: _____   Number of errors made: _____

The Peregrine Falcon Returns

In the 1960s, a small bird of prey called the peregrine falcon was near extinction. A harmful chemical called DDT nearly killed off this species. This chemical was sprayed on crops to control pests. It then washed into lakes and rivers. Fish absorbed this chemical and then were eaten by the peregrines. As a result of this poison, the shells of the peregrine's eggs became too soft to hatch. Soon, this would mean no more peregrines.

Fortunately, people started to do something about this problem. In the United States, the DDT spray was prohibited from use. Yet, other problems remained. In many areas, the natural habitat of the falcons had been destroyed or compromised. That was also a threat to the survival of the birds.

A group of researchers in the United States decided to step in. In 1979, the Eastern Peregrine Recovery Program was launched. Along the East Coast, the researchers began to breed peregrines in captivity. They set up nesting trays where the birds could lay eggs and hatch their young, called "eyas." Then the birds were released. The eyas had not been born in the wild. Would they be able to survive on their own?

Some of the young peregrines were released in cities. There they nested in special boxes on the ledges of tall buildings. Researchers chose the spots because they are like the cliffs where the birds most often dwell. The first year was hazardous for the birds.

Yet, by 1999, the peregrine was off the endangered list of birds in many areas. Human beings had nursed a species back from extinction.

1. What factors caused the near-disappearance of the peregrine falcons?

2. What is "The Peregrine Falcon Returns" mostly about?

Oral Reading Fluency Record Sheet

Name _____ Date _____

Oral Reading Accuracy: _____%   Circle: Fall   Winter   Spring
Oral Reading Fluency Score: _____ words correct per minute
Comprehension Questions Responses
#1 _____
#2 _____

The Peregrine Falcon Returns

In the 1960s, a small bird of prey called the peregrine falcon was near

14 extinction. A harmful chemical called DDT nearly killed off this species.

25 This chemical was sprayed on crops to control pests. It then washed into

38 lakes and rivers. Fish absorbed this chemical and then were eaten by the

51 peregrines. As a result of this poison, the shells of the peregrine's eggs

64 became too soft to hatch. Soon, this would mean no more peregrines.

76 Fortunately, people started to do something about this problem. In the

87 United States, the DDT spray was prohibited from use. Yet, other problems

99 remained. In many areas, the natural habitat of the falcons had been

111 destroyed or compromised. That was also a threat to the survival of the birds.

125 A group of researchers in the United States decided to step in. In 1979,

139 the Eastern Peregrine Recovery Program was launched. Along the East

149 Coast, the researchers began to breed peregrines in captivity. They set up

161 nesting trays where the birds could lay eggs and hatch their young,

173 called "eyas." Then the birds were released. The eyas had not been born in

187 the wild. Would they be able to survive on their own?

198 Some of the young peregrines were released in cities. There they nested

210 in special boxes on the ledges of tall buildings. Researchers chose the spots

223 because they are like the cliffs where the birds most often dwell. The first

237 year was hazardous for the birds.

243 Yet, by 1999, the peregrine was off the endangered list of birds in many

257 areas. Human beings had nursed a species back from extinction. **267**

Number of words read: _____   Number of errors made: _____

Kai and the Elephant

The June sun beat down on Kai's head, and a swarm of flies buzzed about. Kai dreamily lowered his eyelids until the noises around him began to subside. If he remained still, the air grew slightly cooler, and a soft breeze made itself felt.

The low, flat land was dusty with the scarcity of rainfall. Elephants began drifting in the direction of the watering-hole. There was precious little moisture anywhere. Many animals suffered severely; these elephants were fortunate that they had sufficient food and water. The huge beasts were surprisingly peaceful, considering their size. Kai wondered what prevented them from fighting over the watering-hole.

Suddenly, everything changed. A terrible pounding shook the earth.

"Rogue elephant!" somebody cried out. Immediately, a clamor of frightened voices arose. A rogue elephant was a mammoth creature out of control, something like a truck speeding down a road with no one at the wheel. A crazed elephant could inflict serious and lasting damage.

A man came running from nowhere, a length of rope in hand. As the stricken crowd watched, the small man ran up alongside the elephant. He hurled the lasso around the huge beast's neck, pulling on the rope until his tendons bulged. Another man dashed out of the crowd to help. Together, the two sweated and strained until the rogue elephant was stopped.

"Kai, pay attention!" snapped the teacher. "We've come all the way to the zoo, and you just stand there daydreaming!"

1. Which parts of the story were realistic, and which were fantasy?
2. Why would a rogue elephant present a danger?

Oral Reading Fluency Record Sheet

Name _____ Date _____

Oral Reading Accuracy: _____%   Circle: Fall Winter Spring
Oral Reading Fluency Score: _____ words correct per minute
Comprehension Questions Responses
#1 _____
#2 _____

Kai and the Elephant

The June sun beat down on Kai's head, and a swarm of flies buzzed

14   about. Kai dreamily lowered his eyelids until the noises around him began to

27   subside. If he remained still, the air grew slightly cooler, and a soft breeze

41   made itself felt.

44   The low, flat land was dusty with the scarcity of rainfall. Elephants began

57   drifting in the direction of the watering-hole. There was precious little

69   moisture anywhere. Many animals suffered severely; these elephants were

78   fortunate that they had sufficient food and water. The huge beasts were

90   surprisingly peaceful, considering their size. Kai wondered what prevented

99   them from fighting over the watering-hole.

106 Suddenly, everything changed. A terrible pounding shook the earth.

115 "Rogue elephant!" somebody cried out. Immediately, a clamor of

124 frightened voices arose. A rogue elephant was a mammoth creature out of

136 control, something like a truck speeding down a road with no one at the

150 wheel. A crazed elephant could inflict serious and lasting damage.

160 A man came running from nowhere, a length of rope in hand. As the

174 stricken crowd watched, the small man ran up alongside the elephant. He

186 hurled the lasso around the huge beast's neck, pulling on the rope until his

200 tendons bulged. Another man dashed out of the crowd to help. Together, the

213 two sweated and strained until the rogue elephant was stopped.

223 "Kai, pay attention!" snapped the teacher. "We've come all the way to the

236 zoo, and you just stand there daydreaming!" **243**

Number of words read: _____   Number of errors made: _____

Roberto Clemente: The Great One

Roberto Clemente is one of the baseball greats. He had the best throwing arm of any right fielder in the history of the sport. He had the accuracy of an archer and the fluidity of a bull whip. He played in an era when running, fielding, and throwing were judged to be as important as hitting.

Roberto Clemente was born in Puerto Rico in 1934. As a child, he loved sports. He won medals in track and field and the javelin throw. The track practice made him a fast base runner. Hurling the javelin developed his throwing arm. But Clemente loved baseball above all. His career in sports really began when the Pittsburgh Pirates signed him. He would play for the Pirates for all eighteen years of his career.

Clemente's record speaks for itself. He was the National League Batting Champion four times. He was named National League MVP in 1966, and was also the MVP in the 1971 World Series. The man with the fierce right arm was awarded twelve Gold Gloves.

Roberto Clemente was also a hero of another kind. He lost his life helping others. In 1972, Nicaragua was struck by a terrible earthquake. Clemente insisted on aiding the relief effort. He wanted to make a real difference. So he boarded a small cargo plane carrying food and supplies to the victims. On December 31 of that year, the plane went down into the sea. Roberto Clemente's life came to an end.

Fans around the world mourned the passing of the great athlete. He had won his place in the Baseball Hall of Fame. If Babe Ruth was the greatest ever, and Willie Mays the best all around, then surely Roberto Clemente was the most elegant baseball player of all time.

1. What prepared the young Roberto Clemente for his career in baseball?

2. What can you conclude about Clemente on and off the baseball field?

Oral Reading Fluency Record Sheet

Name _____ Date _____

Oral Reading Accuracy: _____%   Circle: Fall   Winter   Spring

Oral Reading Fluency Score: _____ words correct per minute

Comprehension Questions Responses

#1 _____

#2 _____

Roberto Clemente: The Great One

      Roberto Clemente is one of the baseball greats. He had the best throwing

13 arm of any right fielder in the history of the sport. He had the accuracy of an

30 archer and the fluidity of a bull whip. He played in an era when running,

45 fielding, and throwing were judged to be as important as hitting.

56   Roberto Clemente was born in Puerto Rico in 1934. As a child, he loved

70 sports. He won medals in track and field and the javelin throw. The track

84 practice made him a fast base runner. Hurling the javelin developed his

96 throwing arm. But Clemente loved baseball above all. His career in sports

108 really began when the Pittsburgh Pirates signed him. He would play for the

121 Pirates for all eighteen years of his career.

129   Clemente's record speaks for itself. He was the National League Batting

140 Champion four times. He was named National League MVP in 1966, and

152 was also the MVP in the 1971 World Series. The man with the fierce right

167 arm was awarded twelve Gold Gloves.

173   Roberto Clemente was also a hero of another kind. He lost his life

186 helping others. In 1972, Nicaragua was struck by a terrible earthquake.

197 Clemente insisted on aiding the relief effort. He wanted to make a real

210 difference. So he boarded a small cargo plane carrying food and supplies to

223 the victims. On December 31 of that year, the plane went down into the sea.

238 Roberto Clemente's life came to an end.

245   Fans around the world mourned the passing of the great athlete. He had

258 won his place in the Baseball Hall of Fame. If Babe Ruth was the greatest

273 ever, and Willie Mays the best all around, then surely Roberto Clemente was

285 the most elegant baseball player of all time. **294**

Number of words read: _____   Number of errors made: _____

Penelope Joins the Crew

Penelope could barely contain her excitement as the ground team counted down the seconds to lift off. This was her first shuttle flight. It was a miracle that she was on board today. For months, she had begged and pleaded with the administrators at NASA for this opportunity.

She prepared a good argument. "This is 2035, and a student has never been on a shuttle crew. Don't you think it's time for today's youth to join the space program? Think how it will inspire students to study science."

At last, NASA had given its consent, and Penelope found herself a member of the flight crew. Her job had been to memorize basic procedures. She had done this thoroughly, reading the manuals for countless hours.

Take off minus six seconds: the main engines of the shuttle were ignited one by one, and the engines built up to over ninety percent of their maximum thrust. Take off minus three seconds: the shuttle's main engines were in lift-off position. Lift off!

Penelope slowly exhaled with the rest of the nervous crew. They were experienced astronauts, so they knew that take off and landing were risky events for a shuttle flight. There were a few cautious smiles now, which made Penelope feel better, too.

But then, at take off plus 7.7, Penelope stared at the instrument panels in horror. Right now, the main engines were supposed to throttle down to keep the shuttle from breaking apart. But the instrument panel told another story.

Penelope wasted no time. She grabbed Astronaut Thomas and explained what she saw on the instrument panel. Within seconds, the situation had been corrected. The engines throttled down, and the mission was saved.

© Macmillan/McGraw-Hill

1. What went wrong soon after the shuttle lifted off?
2. Why was Penelope able to spot the problem?

Oral Reading Fluency Record Sheet

Name _____ Date _____

Oral Reading Accuracy: _____%   Circle: Fall   Winter   Spring

Oral Reading Fluency Score: _____ words correct per minute

Comprehension Questions Responses

#1 _____

#2 _____

Penelope Joins the Crew

Penelope could barely contain her excitement as the ground team counted

11   down the seconds to lift off. This was her first shuttle flight. It was a miracle

27   that she was on board today. For months, she had begged and pleaded with

41   the administrators at NASA for this opportunity.

48   She prepared a good argument. "This is 2035, and a student has never

61   been on a shuttle crew. Don't you think it's time for today's youth to join the

77   space program? Think how it will inspire students to study science."

88   At last, NASA had given its consent, and Penelope found herself a

100   member of the flight crew. Her job had been to memorize basic procedures.

113   She had done this thoroughly, reading the manuals for countless hours.

124   Take off minus six seconds: the main engines of the shuttle were ignited

137   one by one, and the engines built up to over ninety percent of their maximum

152   thrust. Take off minus three seconds: the shuttle's main engines were in

164   lift-off position. Lift off!

169   Penelope slowly exhaled with the rest of the nervous crew. They were

181   experienced astronauts, so they knew that take off and landing were risky

193   events for a shuttle flight. There were a few cautious smiles now, which

206   made Penelope feel better, too.

211   But then, at take off plus 7.7, Penelope stared at the instrument panels in

225   horror. Right now, the main engines were supposed to throttle down to keep

238   the shuttle from breaking apart. But the instrument panel told another story.

250   Penelope wasted no time. She grabbed Astronaut Thomas and explained

260   what she saw on the instrument panel. Within seconds, the situation had been

273   corrected. The engines throttled down, and the mission was saved. **283**

Number of words read: _____   Number of errors made: _____

The Dangerous Job of the Smoke Jumper

Everyone knows that firefighters have a dangerous job. Perhaps the deadliest firefighting job is that of the smoke jumper. This profession first developed in the 1940s to fight forest fires. Planes deliver the firefighters to remote areas that trucks may have difficulty reaching. Smoke jumpers parachute out of planes into the wilds. They carry their equipment on their backs in seventy-pound packs. This is not a job for the faint of heart. Wild fires can spread quickly, posing a serious threat to the firefighter.

Once on the scene, the smoke jumper has to make quick, sound decisions. He must be aware of the direction and force of the wind, and gauge the fire's condition. In the midst of smoke, flames, and gales, the jumper must remain calm and do the job.

Strength and fitness are also required of the jumper. The jumper must be highly trained because the work is so dangerous. In addition to training, the jumper must have prior expertise fighting forest fires. He then takes an advanced training course. Even seasoned firefighters take instructional courses, which are given in the spring to get teams ready for the fires that break out in summer.

Surprisingly, there are more firefighters applying for these positions than are needed. Perhaps the thrill of parachuting draws some people. Others apply because they realize that their skills are desperately needed. Each year, thousands of acres of forest land burn. These fires destroy trees, plants, animals, and sometimes human beings. It takes many years for the forest to grow back. The smoke jumper represents a powerful weapon in the battle to control forest fires.

1. What do smoke jumpers do?
2. Why are smoke jumpers needed to fight forest fires?

Oral Reading Fluency Record Sheet

Name _____ Date _____

Oral Reading Accuracy: _____%   Circle: Fall   Winter   Spring
Oral Reading Fluency Score: _____ words correct per minute
Comprehension Questions Responses
#1 _____
#2 _____

The Dangerous Job of the Smoke Jumper

	Everyone knows that firefighters have a dangerous job. Perhaps the
10	deadliest firefighting job is that of the smoke jumper. This profession first
22	developed in the 1940s to fight forest fires. Planes deliver the firefighters to
35	remote areas that trucks may have difficulty reaching. Smoke jumpers
45	parachute out of planes into the wilds. They carry their equipment on their
58	backs in seventy-pound packs. This is not a job for the faint of heart. Wild
74	fires can spread quickly, posing a serious threat to the firefighter.
85	Once on the scene, the smoke jumper has to make quick, sound decisions.
98	He must be aware of the direction and force of the wind, and gauge the fire's
114	condition. In the midst of smoke, flames, and gales, the jumper must remain
127	calm and do the job.
132	Strength and fitness are also required of the jumper. The jumper must be
145	highly trained because the work is so dangerous. In addition to training, the
158	jumper must have prior expertise fighting forest fires. He then takes an
170	advanced training course. Even seasoned firefighters take instructional
179	courses, which are given in the spring to get teams ready for the fires that
194	break out in summer.
198	Surprisingly, there are more firefighters applying for these positions than
208	are needed. Perhaps the thrill of parachuting draws some people. Others
219	apply because they realize that their skills are desperately needed. Each year,
231	thousands of acres of forest land burn. These fires destroy trees, plants,
243	animals, and sometimes human beings. It takes many years for the forest to
256	grow back. The smoke jumper represents a powerful weapon in the battle to
269	control forest fires. **272**

Number of words read: _____   Number of errors made: _____

© Macmillan/McGraw-Hill

In the Cornfields

Rachel was walking home from the shopping center when she saw it. For an instant, she thought she was imagining this massed dark funnel because it resembled so closely the photographs of tornadoes she had seen in magazines. After all, the eyes can play bizarre tricks on people. She looked again—this was no fantasy. The dark thing was suspended over the cornfields leering at her.

Rachel had lived in this Midwestern town for only a month. Next week, school would start and then she would not feel so isolated. She had been born and raised in Brooklyn, New York, a metropolis where tornadoes were seldom seen. Now, she stood a mile away from this looming menace.

What had she read about tornado safety? Obviously, a person should not be within miles of one of them. She recalled a manual that advised people in tornado-prone regions to remain in their basements during a tornado and to keep a battery-powered radio with them for updated weather reports. But Rachel was nowhere near her new home on Buell Lane. There were no subway stations to dash into, no conveniently located stores.

As the winds increased and the surrounding sky blackened like a bruise, Rachel shivered. The sky shuddered in reply, whipping the branches of the trees and tearing off the leaves. Rocks skittered down the road and began to fly about as if possessed. There was no more time to ponder. Rachel hurried to the side of the road where a low ditch ran alongside the field. She lay down flat and covered her head with her arms. The tornado blew over the field in a demented fury. Half-an-hour later, Rachel sat up, dazed and filthy from the debris that rained down on her from the storm. The girl from the city of subways and delicatessens had survived her first tornado.

1. What must Rachel have suddenly remembered about tornado safety?

2. What probably makes a tornado particularly dangerous to people outdoors?

© Macmillan/McGraw-Hill

Oral Reading Fluency Record Sheet

Name _____ Date _____

Oral Reading Accuracy: _____%   Circle: Fall   Winter   Spring
Oral Reading Fluency Score: _____ words correct per minute
Comprehension Questions Responses
#1 _____
#2 _____

In the Cornfields

    Rachel was walking home from the shopping center when she saw it. For

13 an instant, she thought she was imagining this massed dark funnel because it

26 resembled so closely the photographs of tornadoes she had seen in magazines.

38 After all, the eyes can play bizarre tricks on people. She looked again—this

52 was no fantasy. The dark thing was suspended over the cornfields leering at her.

66   Rachel had lived in this Midwestern town for only a month. Next week,

79 school would start and then she would not feel so isolated. She had been

93 born and raised in Brooklyn, New York, a metropolis where tornadoes were

105 seldom seen. Now, she stood a mile away from this looming menace.

117   What had she read about tornado safety? Obviously, a person should not

129 be within miles of one of them. She recalled a manual that advised people in

144 tornado-prone regions to remain in their basements during a tornado and to

157 keep a battery-powered radio with them for updated weather reports. But

169 Rachel was nowhere near her new home on Buell Lane. There were no

182 subway stations to dash into, no conveniently located stores.

191   As the winds increased and the surrounding sky blackened like a bruise,

203 Rachel shivered. The sky shuddered in reply, whipping the branches of the

215 trees and tearing off the leaves. Rocks skittered down the road and began to

229 fly about as if possessed. There was no more time to ponder. Rachel hurried

243 to the side of the road where a low ditch ran alongside the field. She lay

259 down flat and covered her head with her arms. The tornado blew over the

273 field in a demented fury. Half-an-hour later, Rachel sat up, dazed and filthy

288 from the debris that rained down on her from the storm. The girl from the

303 city of subways and delicatessens had survived her first tornado. **313**

Number of words read: _____   Number of errors made: _____

Of Mermaids and Manatees

Long ago, sailors believed there were mermaids under the sea. Some people reported sightings of creatures that were half girl, half fish. Mermaids were said to be very beautiful and to sing sweetly. They were considered lucky creatures.

Most likely, sailors were seeing manatees. The manatee, or Sea Cow, is a marine animal found in the Everglades of Florida, the Guianas, and Grand Bahama. Calling a manatee a sea cow is appropriate because the animal is so awkward-looking. It has a rounded body, a blunt muzzle, and small eyes. The manatee can grow to a length of fifteen feet and weigh up to 2,000 pounds!

Unlike its cousin the seal, the manatee cannot leave the sea completely. However, it can thrust its upper body onto the shore to feed on plants. But like the whale, the manatee can only survive in water.

There are now far fewer manatees than there were in the past. In fact, some people say this mammal may become extinct. A disease has already destroyed many manatees. Human beings have not always helped, either. Some hunt the manatee, while factories pollute the waters of oceans and rivers. Motor boats also are responsible for reducing the manatee population.

Today, many people in Florida have become concerned about the manatee. Scientists study the behavior of this animal in order to help save it. Rescue groups work to aid manatees that become stranded on the beach. Recently, a movie was made about the rescue of two manatees that were trapped in a storm drain. This creature, though not as pretty as the mythical mermaid, has certainly won the hearts of animal lovers.

1. How does the manatee differ from the seal?

2. What did the people who made the movie about the manatees hope to do?

Oral Reading Fluency Record Sheet

Name _____ Date _____

Oral Reading Accuracy: _____%   Circle: Fall   Winter   Spring

Oral Reading Fluency Score: _____ words correct per minute

Comprehension Questions Responses

#1 _____

#2 _____

Of Mermaids and Manatees

Long ago, sailors believed there were mermaids under the sea. Some

11 people reported sightings of creatures that were half girl, half fish. Mermaids

23 were said to be very beautiful and to sing sweetly. They were considered

36 lucky creatures.

38 Most likely, sailors were seeing manatees. The manatee, or Sea Cow, is

50 a marine animal found in the Everglades of Florida, the Guianas, and Grand

63 Bahama. Calling a manatee a sea cow is appropriate because the animal is so

77 awkward-looking. It has a rounded body, a blunt muzzle, and small eyes. The

91 manatee can grow to a length of fifteen feet and weigh up to 2,000 pounds!

106 Unlike its cousin the seal, the manatee cannot leave the sea completely.

118 However, it can thrust its upper body onto the shore to feed on plants. But

133 like the whale, the manatee can only survive in water.

143 There are now far fewer manatees than there were in the past. In fact,

157 some people say this mammal may become extinct. A disease has already

169 destroyed many manatees. Human beings have not always helped, either.

179 Some hunt the manatee, while factories pollute the waters of oceans and

191 rivers. Motor boats also are responsible for reducing the manatee population.

202 Today, many people in Florida have become concerned about the

212 manatee. Scientists study the behavior of this animal in order to help save it.

226 Rescue groups work to aid manatees that become stranded on the beach.

238 Recently, a movie was made about the rescue of two manatees that were

251 trapped in a storm drain. This creature, though not as pretty as the mythical

265 mermaid, has certainly won the hearts of animal lovers. **274**

Number of words read: _____   Number of errors made: _____

Answers

Page 28

1. Rita was upset about the survival of the wild kittens. She knew they would be destroyed if she let her father and other farmers know that they were on the property.
2. Wild cats survive by hunting birds, fowl, and other small animals.

Page 30

1. Theodore Roosevelt was a determined man who knew how to make his ideas a reality.
2. John Stevens changed the plan for the canal by having workers construct a "lake and lock" system that elevated water so that ships could pass over rocky areas; the first plan had involved digging to sea level.

Page 32

1. The carp in Grandmother's fishpond brought the ring to Kira in its mouth.
2. Kira threw the ring back into the pond because she was frightened by the idea that the ring had given her great power.

Page 34

1. Alice began to feel bad about herself because she found the scar on her eye embarrassing.
2. Dealing with challenges helped make Walker a good writer.

Page 36

1. They were both treated as outsiders. Neither boy probably had friends.
2. Amos did not have the same advantages as the other students. Amit's experience was different. He came from another country.

Page 38

1. Ebu Gogo lived in caves on the Indonesian island of Flores.
2. The author's viewpoint is that Ebu Gogo was a real species that is now extinct. Although the fantasy connection is interesting, Ebu Gogo were not hobbits.

Page 40

1. The theme of the story is that imagined threats may be far worse than the reality.
2. The strange sounds that Ethan heard were caused by the falling of tree branches in the storm, and his parents trying to drag the branches out of the driveway.

Page 42

1. An earthquake, volcanic eruption or landslide takes place along a fault; a column of water is forced up and travels toward the shore.
2. Tsunamis, powerful tidal waves, develop under the ocean and hit coastal areas with enormous force, often causing terrible destruction.

Page 44

1. Mr. Lincoln believed that slavery should not be permitted to spread across the land, as it would divide the nation.
2. Sallie learned that it was in the best interests of any group of people to work together, and not to oppose one another. She applied this lesson to her own family as well as to her country.

Page 46

1. The dancer Ruth St. Denis first inspired Martha Graham to learn modern dance.
2. The author wrote this article to describe a pioneer of modern dance who brought her personal vision to her work.

Answers *(continued)*

Page 48

1. Two cousins have to decide what to do with some buried artifacts that once belonged to an ancient people.
2. The fragments of pottery had probably come from the burial of an important Native American leader.

Page 50

1. The near-disappearance of the peregrine falcon was caused by human interference with the birds' natural habitat and life-cycle; the destruction of wilderness was one factor, and the use of DDT was another.
2. "The Peregrine Falcon Returns" is mostly about how the peregrine falcon was rescued from extinction when researchers decided to reverse the harm done to the population by people.

Page 52

1. The heat of the day and the presence of elephants was realistic; the emergence of a rogue elephant and the daring feats of the two men were Kai's fantasy or daydream.
2. A rogue elephant would present a danger because it could easily trample anything or anybody in its way. Its massive size would make it a deadly force to be controlled.

Page 54

1. Running track and field and throwing the javelin prepared Roberto Clemente for a career in baseball. He worked on his speed while running track, and strengthened his aim and accuracy through the javelin throw.
2. You can conclude that Clemente was equally dedicated to doing his best both on and off the baseball field. He worked hard to perfect his game, and he did not spare himself when it came to working on behalf of others.

Page 56

1. The main engines did not throttle down, which they had to do in order to keep the shuttle from breaking apart.
2. Penelope was able to spot the problem because she had carefully studied the flight manual and was alert to all stages of take off.

Page 58

1. Smoke jumpers parachute out of planes into burning forestland. They help fight raging fires in areas that people could not reach otherwise. Smoke jumpers must be fit and trained to perform well under difficult conditions.
2. Smoke jumpers are used to fight forest fires because often, trucks cannot get to remote areas of wilderness.

Page 60

1. Rachel must have remembered that the manual advised people outdoors in a tornado to take cover in a ditch and wait for the storm to pass by.
2. What makes a tornado particularly dangerous to people outdoors is the high winds that can blow heavy objects about and even knock a grown person flat.

Page 62

1. The manatee differs from the seal because it cannot remain out of water for very long.
2. The people who made the movie about the manatees hoped to persuade audiences that manatees are worth saving.

Overview

The **Informal Reading Inventory (IRI)** is an individually-administered diagnostic that assesses a student's reading comprehension and reading accuracy. The IRI measures three reading levels: independent, instructional and frustrational. The independent reading level is when a student reads without help from the teacher. To be independent, the student should accurately decode at least 95% of the words and comprehend 90% of the material. The instructional reading level is reached when a student accurately decodes at least 90% of the words and comprehends at least 60% of the material. To obtain a frustrational level, the student decodes 89% or less of the words and can comprehend only 50% of the material.

At each grade level, there are two fiction and two non-fiction reading passages. These passages alternate between oral reading and silent reading as an IRI tests for both oral and silent reading comprehension. To assess the student's comprehension, there are three literal (L) questions, one vocabulary (V) question, and one interpretive (I) question per passage. On the teacher recording sheet, there is a table for each oral reading passage to help identify the student's reading level. This level is based on a combined score of comprehension points and word recognition errors. For each silent reading passage, the total number of comprehension points is used to determine a reading level.

Informal Reading Inventory

The IRI consists of reading passages, teacher recording sheets, and graded word lists for grades 1–6. The reading passages appear on a reproducible student page. Each passage is ten sentences long and consists of Dolch words in Grades 1–3 and Harris-Jacobsen words in 4–6. The reading difficulty of the passages is near the midpoint of each grade level. There is a teacher recording sheet following each student passage that includes the passage, five questions, and a table to determine the appropriate reading level.

How to Use the IRI

Determine reading levels for both oral and silent reading comprehension. Before a student reads a passage, administer the graded word lists to determine the appropriate grade level. These lists span grades 1–6 and consist of Dolch words, story words, and words that contain appropriate sound-spelling sequences for that level. Teachers should start administering the lists with grade 1 to obtain a general estimate of the student's independent, instructional, and frustrational reading levels.

The correct instructional level is when the student makes one error. Students who make two errors should go back to the previous list and start reading at that level.

Use this grade level to start administering the oral and silent reading passages, and as a quick assessment of basic sight word knowledge, and phonics and structural analysis skills.

Administering the IRI

The IRI is organized by grade level. In order to administer the IRI efficiently, you should be familiar with directions, passages, and questions. To administer the IRI, follow these procedures:

1. Make a copy of all of the graded word lists.

2. Place the grade one word list in front of the student and say, *"Here are some words I would like you to read aloud. Try to read them all, even if you are not sure what some of the words are. Let's begin by reading the words on this list."*

3. If the student is able to easily read these words, this early success may build the student's confidence. If you feel certain that a third-grade student can read above a third-grade level, then begin with a higher list. On the other hand, if a first-grade student misses two words on the first-grade word list, then stop. You should then read the passage aloud and have the student answer the comprehension questions. This activity turns into a listening comprehension inventory. Use the scoring table for the silent reading comprehension passage to determine a reading level for listening comprehension.

4. Record words pronounced correctly with a (✓) mark on the sheet that shows each graded word list. Write incorrect responses on the line next to the word.

5. Have the student continue reading higher-level lists until one error is made.

6. After the student misses two words, stop the testing, collect the test sheets, and complete the results in the graded word list section on the sheet.

7. Follow these directions to score the graded word list.
   - The highest level at which the student misses zero words is the student's independent reading level.
   - The highest level at which the student misses one word is the student's instructional reading level.
   - The highest level at which the student misses two words is the frustrational reading level.
   - If the student scores independent, instructional, or frustrational at more than one level, assign the score to the highest level.

8. Select the first passage for the student to read orally. Have the student start reading on the instructional level determined by the graded word lists.

9. Begin by saying, *"I have some passages for you to read. Read the first one aloud. If you find a hard word, try to read it as best you can and continue reading. It is important to remember what you read so you can answer questions at the end."*

10. While the student reads out loud, code the errors or miscues on the scoring sheet. Do not provide any prompting if a student hesitates over a word. If a student hesitates longer than five seconds, simply tell the word to the student.

11. When the student has completed the passage or story, take it away. The student cannot refer to it while answering the questions.

12. Ask the student the comprehension questions as shown on the teacher recording sheet for the passage. Mark correct answers with a point value on the line provided. The point value is in parentheses at the end of each question. A perfect score is 10 points. Interpretive questions are given four points. Vocabulary questions are given three points. Literal questions are given one point. The total number of points that a student earns is the comprehension score. (Instructions for scoring word accuracy and comprehension questions will be provided on page 71.)

At this point, you will have the student shift from oral to silent reading.

13. After scoring the first oral passage, say, *"Read this passage to yourself and try to remember what you read so that you can answer questions at the end."*

14. Give the student the "B" passage next. If the student began with the 1A oral passage, then continue with 1B silent passage.

15. When the student has finished reading the passage, ask the questions based on the passage. Mark the point values that the student earned on the lines provided, and total the number of points earned at the bottom of the questions.

16. After giving the first oral and silent reading passages, determine whether the student has been able to read them at an independent level. If both the oral and silent passages were at the student's independent reading level, continue with the next higher oral reading passage. Then follow with the corresponding silent passage until the frustration level is reached. In many cases, a student will reach frustration level on either oral or silent reading but not both. In these instances, continue with either the oral or silent reading passages until the student reaches frustration level on both.

17. After giving the first oral and silent reading passages, determine if the student is reading at the independent level on either or both passages. If not, give an easier oral and silent passage until both oral and silent frustration levels are reached. The goal is that a student should have an independent, instructional and frustrational reading level for both oral and silent reading.

Code for Marking Word Recognition Errors

Each word recognition error is counted as one error. Never count more than one error on any one word.

Examples	Marking Word Recognition Errors
✓ ✓ ✓ The baby cried	1. Put a check mark over words read correctly.
✓ ✓ My friend (went)	2. Circle omissions.
✓ eats ✓ ✓ He ate the pie	3. Draw a line above words that are read with substitutions. Write the substitution above the line.
✓ T ✓ Why are you	4. Place a T above a word that you need to tell student.
✓ ✓ eating R dinner	5. Place an R next to a word the student repeats.
✓ ✓ ✓ See/S a kind person. She	6. Place the student's initial response and an S above a word that is self corrected. Note: Do not score as an error.
✓ ✓ a (red) apple	7. Use parentheses ( ) to enclose a word that is inserted.

Example of a Passage with Coded Word Recognition Errors

<u>bought</u>

✓ ✓ ✓ ✓ ✓ ✓ ✓ ✓ ✓ ✓ ✓

Pam went to the store to buy a cake for the surprise party.

✓ ✓ ✓ ✓ ✓ ✓   T

The cake was for her mom's birthday.

✓ ✓ ✓   T   ✓ ✓ ✓   like/S   ch/S

Pam got a chocolate cake. Her R mom (really) loves chocolate.

Here is what the teacher heard as the student read the passage. The words in italics are the actual words that the student read.

"Pam went to the store to bought a cake for the surprise party. The cake was for her mom's birthday. Pam got a (after five seconds the teacher produced "chocolate") *cake. Her . . . Her mom really likes loves ch . . . ch . . . chocolate."*

The student made four mistakes that are to be scored as errors:

(1) *bought* substituted for *buy*

(2) *birthday* pronounced by the teacher

(3) *chocolate* pronounced by the teacher

(4) *really* inserted

The self correction for *ch* is not counted as an error.

The self correction for *likes* is not counted as an error.

The repetition for *her* is not counted as an error.

This passage is at the frustration level for this student.

Procedure for Scoring Oral Reading Passages

1. Count the total number of scorable errors as outlined in numbers 1–4 and 7 in the **Code for Marking Word Recognition Errors**. Write the total number of errors in the space indicated on the teacher recording sheet. Insertions, substitutions, words told to the student by the teacher, and omissions, are counted as errors at each occurrence. Words that are self-corrected and repeated are not counted as errors.

2. If a student mispronounces a proper name, count it as one error for the entire passage, even if the student mispronounces the same name again.

3. On the teacher recording sheet, a table follows the set of questions for each oral reading passage. Across the table is a series of numbers to designate the number of word recognition errors. In the column on the left hand side is a series of numbers that show the number of points earned. Locate the number of word recognition errors made by the student in that passage and circle the appropriate number. Then locate the number of points earned and draw a circle around that number. Find the point where the two circled numbers intersect. In that space, you will note the following symbols: the (✓) means the student is reading on an independent level; the (*) means the student is reading on an instructional level; and the (–) means the student is reading at a frustrational level.

Scoring Table for Oral Reading				
	# of Word Recognition Errors			
Total Points Earned	0–4	5–7	8+	Reading Level
7–10 pts	✓	*	–	Independent ☐
4–6 pts	*	*	–	Instructional ☐
0–3 pts	–	–	–	Frustrational ✔

In the above table, for example, the student has made eight word recognition errors and earned two comprehension points. The student answered two literal questions correctly. These two figures intersect in an area marked with a hyphen (–). This means the student is reading on a frustrational level; the box to the right of the frustrational level is checked.

Procedure for Scoring Silent Reading Passages

1. Add up the number of points earned from the five comprehension questions.

2. There is a table below the questions that follow each silent reading passage on the teacher recording sheet. Look at the table to see which level the student is reading at, based on the number of points earned. In the following example, the student earned three points. This would place the student in the range indicated by 0–3 in the table. This corresponds to the frustrational level; the box to the right of the frustrational level is checked.

Scoring Table for Silent Reading	
Total Points Earned	Reading Level
7–10 pts	Independent ☐
4–6 pts	Instructional ☐
0–3 pts	Frustrational ✔

© Macmillan/McGraw-Hill

Individual Graded Word Lists

Grade 1	Grade 2	Grade 3
mother	prize	started
could	noise	lonely
family	understood	thought
there	another	breathe
said	piece	enough
people	trouble	prepare
bake	easier	actually
what	afraid	waist
three	scare	earn
town	always	delighted

Grade 4	Grade 5	Grade 6
adopted	approaching	countryside
communicate	crystals	heroism
bracelet	development	consented
announced	territory	mercilessly
choice	astonished	appalling
requires	coarse	veterinarian
objects	moisture	spectacle
bulge	luxuries	emperor
gravity	irregular	ravenous
resulting	resemble	exceptional

Diagnostic Assessment: IRI • Grades 1–6

Recording Sheet for Individual Graded Word Lists

Grade 1

mother _____

could _____

family _____

there _____

said _____

people _____

bake _____

what _____

three _____

town _____

Grade 2

prize _____

noise _____

understood _____

another _____

piece _____

trouble _____

easier _____

afraid _____

scare _____

always _____

Grade 3

started _____

lonely _____

thought _____

breathe _____

enough _____

prepare _____

actually _____

waist _____

earn _____

delighted _____

Grade 4

adopted _____

communicate _____

bracelet _____

announced _____

choice _____

requires _____

objects _____

bulge _____

gravity _____

resulting _____

Grade 5

approaching _____

crystals _____

development _____

territory _____

astonished _____

coarse _____

moisture _____

luxuries _____

irregular _____

resemble _____

Grade 6

countryside _____

heroism _____

consented _____

mercilessly _____

appalling _____

veterinarian _____

spectacle _____

emperor _____

ravenous _____

exceptional _____

Grade 1

mother

could

family

there

said

people

bake

what

three

town

prize

noise

understood

another

piece

trouble

easier

afraid

scare

always

started

lonely

thought

breathe

enough

prepare

actually

waist

earn

delighted

Grade 4

adopted

communicate

bracelet

announced

choice

requires

objects

bulge

gravity

resulting

Grade 5

approaching

crystals

development

territory

astonished

coarse

moisture

luxuries

irregular

resemble

countryside

heroism

consented

mercilessly

appalling

veterinarian

spectacle

emperor

ravenous

exceptional

Sam

Ana was so sad.

She was moving out of town.

They could not take her black cat, Sam.

The new house was just too little for pets.

Ana let a good friend take Sam.

Ana liked her new home, but she missed Sam.

One day, Ana went to open the door.

There was Sam!

He had walked for days and days to find Ana.

Ana's mother now said he could stay.

Passage 1A Oral—Fiction

Sam

Ana *was so* sad. *She was* moving *out of* town. *They could not take her black* cat, Sam. *The new* house *was just too little for* pets. Ana *let a good* friend *take* Sam.

Ana liked *her new* home, *but she* missed Sam. *One* day, Ana *went to open the* door. *There was* Sam! *He had* walked *for* days *and* days *to find* Ana. Ana's mother *now said he could* stay.

(71 words) (44 Dolch Words) Number of Word Recognition Errors _____

Questions

L 1. _____ Where was Ana moving? [Out of town] (1 pt.)

L 2. _____ Who was Sam? [Ana's black cat] (1 pt.)

L 3. _____ Why couldn't Sam go to the new house? [The new house was too little for pets.] (1 pt.)

V 4. _____ What did the story mean when it said that Ana "missed" Sam? [Ana wished he was with her.] (3 pts.)

I 5. _____ What did Sam do that would make you think he loved Ana? [He walked for days and days to find her.] (4 pts.)

Total # of points earned _____

	# of Word Recognition Errors			
Total Points Earned	**0–4**	**5–7**	**8+**	**Reading Level**
7–10 pts	✓	*	–	Independent ☐
4–6 pts	*	*	–	Instructional ☐
0–3 pts	–	–	–	Frustrational ☐

Scoring Table for Oral Reading

The Bake Sale

Mrs. Park's class wanted to help people in need.

Mrs. Park said, "We have to make money.

How can we do this?"

"I know what we can do," Ron said.

"We can bake cakes and other foods people like.

Then, we can have a bake sale."

That is just what the class did.

All the children helped make the food.

A lot of hungry people came to eat it.

Soon, the class had money for people in need.

Passage 1B Silent—Fiction

The Bake Sale

Mrs. Park's class wanted to help people in need. Mrs. Park said, "We have to make money. How can we do this?"

"I know what we can do," Ron said. "We can bake cakes and other foods people like. Then, we can have a bake sale."

That is just what the class did. All the children helped make the food. A lot of hungry people came to eat it. Soon, the class had money for people in need.

(78 Words)

Questions

L 1. _____ Who was it that the class wanted to help? [People in need] (1 pt.)

L 2. _____ What did Ron say the class could bake? [Cakes and other foods people like.] (1 pt.)

L 3. _____ What did all the children help to do? [Make the food] (1 pt.)

V 4. _____ The story says, "A lot of hungry people came to eat it." What does *hungry* mean? [Wanting or needing food] (3 pts.)

I 5. _____ Who gave the class the money for the people in need? [The people who paid for food at the bake sale] (4 pts.)

Total # of points earned _____

Scoring Table for Silent Reading	
Total Points Earned	**Reading Level**
7–10 pts	Independent ☐
4–6 pts	Instructional ☐
0–3 pts	Frustrational ☐

School for Clowns

Did you know that there is a clown school?

Clowns go to school to learn to be funny.

They learn how to move in funny ways.

They find out how to run, fall, and jump.

They must make every move look easy.

In school, clowns plan how they will look.

They put on funny pants and tops.

They get into big shoes.

Clowns also put on funny face paint.

They do all this just to make people smile.

Diagnostic Assessment: IRI • Grade 1

Passage 1C Oral—Nonfiction

School for Clowns

Did you know that there is a clown school? Clowns *go to* school *to learn to be funny. They* learn *how to* move *in funny* ways. *They find out how to run, fall, and jump. They must make every* move *look* easy. *In* school, clowns plan *how they will* look. *They put on funny* pants *and* tops. *They get into big* shoes. Clowns also *put on funny* face paint. *They do all this just to make* people smile.

(78 words) (56 Dolch words) Number of Word Recognition Errors _____

Questions

L 1. _____ Why do clowns go to school? [To find out how to be funny] (1 pt.)

L 2. _____ To move in funny ways, clowns find out how to run, jump, and what? [How to fall] (1 pt.)

V 3. _____ The passage says, "They must make every move look easy." What does *easy* mean? [Not hard] (3 pts.)

L 4. _____ Other than funny pants and tops, what do clowns get into? [Big shoes] (1 pt.)

I 5. _____ What is the job of a clown? [To make people smile] (4 pts.)

Total # of points earned _____

	Scoring Table for Oral Reading			
	# of Word Recognition Errors			
Total Points Earned	**0–5**	**6–9**	**10+**	**Reading Level**
7–10 pts	✓	*	–	Independent ☐
4–6 pts	*	*	–	Instructional ☐
0–3 pts	–	–	–	Frustrational ☐

Houses

Our houses are places where we feel safe.
It is the place we like to be with our family.
We can stay in when the weather is bad.
We feel good inside our houses.
You can see that all houses are not the same.
There are wood houses and stone houses.
There are even snow houses!
Some houses are big and some are little.
Some have just one floor.
Others are two and even three floors high.
What is the house that you live in like?

Passage 1D Silent—Nonfiction

Houses

Our houses are places where we feel safe. It is the place we like to be with our family. We can stay in when the weather is bad. We feel good inside our houses.

You can see that all houses are not the same. There are wood houses and stone houses. There are even snow houses! Some houses are big and some are little. Some have just one floor. Others are two and even three floors high. What is the house that you live in like?

(86 words)

Questions

L 1. _____ Where do we feel safe? [In our houses] (1 pt.)

L 2. _____ Who do we like to be with in our houses? [Family] (1 pt.)

L 3. _____ How do we feel inside our houses when the weather is bad outside? [Good] (1 pt.)

I 4. _____ Which kind of house would you see in just cold places? [Snow house] (4 pts.)

V 5. _____ The passage says, "Others are two and even three floors high." What does *high* mean? [From top to bottom] (3 pts.)

Total # of points earned _____

Scoring Table for Silent Reading	
Total Points Earned	**Reading Level**
7–10 pts	Independent ☐
4–6 pts	Instructional ☐
0–3 pts	Frustrational ☐

The Race

One day, Tom saw some boys having a race after school. Tom said, "I would like to be a fast runner like those boys."

Tom began to run every day before and after school. Each day, he was able to run faster than the day before. Soon he could run as fast as the other boys. Tom did not win his first few races, but he would not give up.

The next year, there was a race for all the boys at school. Many of the boys ran fast, but Tom ran faster. The other boys ran hard to catch up with him, but not one could do it. Tom won the race and took home the first prize.

Passage 2A Oral—Fiction

The Race

One day, Tom *saw some* boys having *a* race *after* school. Tom *said,* "*I would like to be a fast* runner *like those* boys."

Tom began *to run every* day *before and after* school. Each day, *he was* able *to run* faster than *the* day *before. Soon he could run as fast as the* other boys. Tom *did not* win *his first* few races, *but he would not give up.*

The next year, *there was a* race *for all the* boys at school. *Many of the* boys *ran fast, but* Tom *ran* faster. *The* other boys *ran* hard *to* catch *up with him, but not one could do it.* Tom won *the* race *and* took home *the first* prize.

(119 words) (77 Dolch words) Number of Word Recognition Errors _____

Questions

L 1. _____ What did Tom see that made him want to be a fast runner? [Some boys having a race] (1 pt.)

L 2. _____ What did Tom do every day before and after school? [He ran.] (1 pt.)

I 3. _____ What did Tom do that would make you think he sticks with something even if things don't go his way? [He did not win the first few races, but he would not give up.] (4 pts.)

V 4. _____ The story says, "The other boys ran hard to catch up with him, but not one could do it." What does "catch up" mean? [Get closer to, or come up to] (3 pts.)

L 5. _____ Why did Tom take home the first prize? [Because he won the race] (1 pt.)

Total # of points earned _____

	Scoring Table for Oral Reading			
	# of Word Recognition Errors			
Total Points Earned	**0–6**	**7–11**	**12+**	**Reading Level**
7–10 pts	✓	*	–	Independent ☐
4–6 pts	*	*	–	Instructional ☐
0–3 pts	–	–	–	Frustrational ☐

Kim and Brownie

Kim had a hard time training her new dog, Brownie. He would not do anything that she told him to do. She could not even get him to come when she called him. Then, one day, Kim saw that Brownie did not move when a loud noise went off.

It was then that she understood that Brownie couldn't hear. Kim found out how to train Brownie by using hand signals. To get Brownie to come, she raised her arm up over her head with her hand facing down.

If she wanted him to sit, she would move her arm down with her hand facing up. Brownie learned fast and was soon doing everything Kim asked of him.

Kim felt very lucky that Brownie was her dog.

Passage 2B Silent—Fiction

Kim and Brownie

Kim had a hard time training her new dog, Brownie. He would not do anything that she told him to do. She could not even get him to come when she called him. Then, one day, Kim saw that Brownie would not move when a loud noise went off.

It was then that she understood that Brownie couldn't hear. Kim found out how to train Brownie by using hand signals. To get Brownie to come, she raised her arm up over her head with her hand facing down.

If she wanted him to sit, she would move her arm down with her hand facing up. Brownie learned fast and was soon doing everything Kim asked of him.

Kim felt very lucky that Brownie was her dog.

(126 words)

Questions

L 1. _____ Who was Brownie? [Kim's new dog] (1 pt.)

L 2. _____ What made Kim understand that Brownie couldn't hear? [He would not move when a loud noise went off.] (1 pt.)

V 3. _____ The story says, "Kim found out how to train Brownie by using hand signals." What does the word *signals* mean? [Signs] (3 pts.)

L 4. _____ What signal did Kim use to get Brownie to sit? [Moved her arm down with her hand facing up] (1 pt.)

I 5. _____ What did Brownie do that would make you think he was smart? [He learned fast and was soon doing everything Kim asked of him.] (4 pts.)

Total # of points earned _____

Scoring Table for Silent Reading	
Total Points Earned	**Reading Level**
7–10 pts	Independent ☐
4–6 pts	Instructional ☐
0–3 pts	Frustrational ☐

Bears

Bears are big animals covered with fur. Their legs are short and fat, but they can run very fast. They can also stand up on their back legs and walk like people do.

Bears are mainly colored black, brown, and white. Black bears, which are around five feet, are not as big as brown or white bears. Black and brown bears climb trees to get away from trouble. Both of these bears eat plants, fruit, and animals.

The white bears are called polar bears, and they live on the ice in very cold places. They are great swimmers, and they swim from one piece of ice to another looking for food. These bears eat just meat, and mostly sea animals.

Passage 2C Oral—Nonfiction

Bears

Bears *are big* animals covered *with* fur. *Their* legs *are* short *and* fat, *but they can run very fast. They* can also stand *up on their* back legs *and walk like* people *do.*

Bears *are* mainly colored *black, brown, and white. Black* bears, *which are around five* feet, *are not as big as brown or white* bears. *Black and brown* bears climb trees *to get away from* trouble. *Both of these* bears *eat* plants, fruit, *and* animals.

The white bears *are* called polar bears, *and they live on the* ice *in very cold* places. *They are* great swimmers, *and they* swim *from one* piece *of* ice *to* another looking *for* food. *These* bears *eat just* meat, and mostly sea animals.

(120 words) (75 Dolch words) Number of Word Recognition Errors _____

Questions

L 1. ____ What are bears covered with? [Fur] (1 pt.)

I 2. ____ What does the passage say that lets you know polar bears are over five feet tall? [Black bears, which are around five feet, are not as big as brown or white bears.] (4 pts.)

V 3. ____ The passage says, "Black and brown bears climb trees to get away from trouble." What does the word *trouble* mean? [A bad situation] (3 pts.)

L 4. ____ Where do polar bears live? [On the ice in very cold places] (1 pt.)

L 5. ____ What do polar bears eat? [Meat, mostly sea animals] (1 pt.)

Total # of points earned _____

Scoring Table for Oral Reading				
	# of Word Recognition Errors			
Total Points Earned	**0–6**	**7–11**	**12+**	**Reading Level**
7–10 pts	✓	*	–	Independent ☐
4–6 pts	*	*	–	Instructional ☐
0–3 pts	–	–	–	Frustrational ☐

About Fire

When people found out how to make fire, their lives became easier. Fire has been around from the days when people lived in caves. Cave people would use fire to stay warm. They also found that they could see more in the dark with the fires going. And many animals like tigers and lions are afraid of fire, so people used fires at night to scare these animals off.

Soon, people found out how to cook over an open fire. Then they made ovens by stacking rocks up over the fires. In these ovens, they baked bread and other good foods. After people found out how to store food, they did not have to go hunting every day. There was always something to eat.

Passage 2D Silent—Nonfiction

About Fire

When people found out how to make fire, their lives became easier. Fire has been around from the days when people lived in caves. Cave people would use fire to stay warm. They also found that they could see more in the dark with the fires going. And many animals like tigers and lions are afraid of fire, so people used fires at night to scare these animals off.

Soon, people found out how to cook over an open fire. Then they made ovens by stacking rocks up over the fires. In these ovens, they baked bread and other good foods. After people found out how to store food, they did not have to go hunting every day. There was always something to eat.

(124 words)

Questions

L 1. _____ What happened to people's lives when they found out how to make fire? [Their lives became easier.] (1 pt.)

L 2. _____ What was one way that cave people used fire? [To stay warm, to see in the dark, or to keep animals away] (1 pt.)

V 3. _____ The passage says, "And many animals like tigers and lions are afraid of fire, so people used fires at night to scare these animals off." What does the word *afraid* mean? [Scared] (3 pts.)

L 4. _____ How did people make ovens? [They stacked rocks up over the fires.] (1 pt.)

I 5. _____ After people found out how to cook and store food, what did they eat when they didn't go hunting? [The stored food] (4 pts.)

Total # of points earned _____

Scoring Table for Silent Reading	
Total Points Earned	**Reading Level**
7–10 pts	Independent ☐
4–6 pts	Instructional ☐
0–3 pts	Frustrational ☐

The Dog Walker

Summer vacation had just started, and Earl was thinking about how to spend his time. Earl liked to read, but he didn't want to spend the whole vacation just reading. He also liked to do things and go places with his friends, but many of them were away for the summer. Then Earl got the idea that it would be wise to try to earn some money.

While playing with his dog, Earl suddenly had a thought. Perhaps people would pay him to walk their dogs. Earl went to the houses of people he knew had dogs, like Mrs. Green. Because she was old and had trouble getting around, she was delighted to hire Earl to walk her big brown dog. In all, Earl was able to find seven people to hire him. By the end of the summer, he was able to buy a new bike.

Passage 3A Oral—Fiction

The Dog Walker

Summer vacation *had just* started, *and* Earl *was* thinking *about how to* spend *his* time. Earl liked *to read, but he* didn't *want to* spend *the* whole vacation *just* reading. *He* also liked *to do* things *and go* places *with his* friends, *but many of them were away for the* summer. *Then* Earl *got the* idea *that it would be* wise *to try to* earn *some* money.

While playing *with his* dog, Earl suddenly *had a* thought. Perhaps people *would* pay *him to walk their* dogs. Earl *went to the* houses *of* people *he* knew *had* dogs, *like* Mrs. Green. *Because she was old and had* trouble getting *around, she was* delighted *to* hire Earl *to walk her big brown* dog. *In all,* Earl *was* able *to find seven* people *to* hire *him. By the* end *of the* summer, *he was* able *to buy a new* bike.

(147 words) (92 Dolch Words) Number of Word Recognition Errors _____

Questions

L 1. _____ Why couldn't Earl spend time with his friends? [Because many were away for the summer] (1 pt.)

L 2. _____ What was Earl doing when he thought about walking dogs for money? [Playing with his dog] (1 pt.)

V 3. _____ The story says, "Because she was old and had trouble getting around, she was delighted to hire Earl to walk her big brown dog." What does the word *delighted* mean? [Very happy] (3 pts.)

L 4. _____ How many people hired Earl? [Seven] (1 pt.)

I 5. _____ Where did Earl get the money to pay for his new bike? [From walking the dogs] (4 pts.)

Total # of points earned _____

Scoring Table for Oral Reading				
	# of Word Recognition Errors			
Total Points Earned	**0–8**	**9–14**	**15+**	**Reading Level**
7–10 pts	✓	*	–	Independent ☐
4–6 pts	*	*	–	Instructional ☐
0–3 pts	–	–	–	Frustrational ☐

Lonely Nina

Nina had never felt as lonely as she did at her new school. She had moved to town over a month ago, and she still had not made any friends. As she sat eating her lunch, she listened to Jen and the other girls from her class talk and laugh. Afraid that they wouldn't like her, she thought it best to keep to herself.

All of a sudden, Nina heard Jen start to choke on some food. When she saw that the girl couldn't breathe, Nina rushed over. She put her arms around Jen's waist from the back and pressed in with her fist. The food came out, and Jen began to take in air.

When she could talk, Jen thanked Nina and asked her to join the other girls. "I would have asked you before," Jen said, "but you always seemed to want to be by yourself."

Passage 3B Silent—Fiction

Lonely Nina

Nina had never felt as lonely as she did at her new school. She had moved to town over a month ago, and she still had not made any friends. As she sat eating her lunch, she listened to Jen and the other girls from her class talk and laugh. Afraid that they wouldn't like her, she thought it best to keep to herself.

All of a sudden, Nina heard Jen start to choke on some food. When she saw that the girl couldn't breathe, Nina rushed over. She put her arms around Jen's waist from the back and pressed in with her fist. The food came out, and Jen began to take in air.

When she could talk, Jen thanked Nina and asked her to join the other girls. "I would have asked you before," Jen said, "but you always seemed to want to be by yourself."

(148 words)

Questions

L 1. _____ How did Nina feel at the beginning of the story? [Lonely] (1 pt.)

L 2. _____ Why did Nina keep to herself? [Because she was afraid the other children wouldn't like her] (1 pt.)

V 3. _____ The story says, "When she saw that the girl couldn't breathe, Nina rushed over." What does the word *breathe* mean? [Take in air] (3 pts.)

L 4. _____ What did Jen do as soon as she could talk? [Jen thanked Nina and asked her to join the other girls.] (1 pt.)

I 5. _____ Why didn't Nina make friends? [Because she kept to herself and did not try to talk to the other children] (4 pts.)

Total # of points earned _____

Scoring Table for Silent Reading	
Total Points Earned	**Reading Level**
7–10 pts	Independent ☐
4–6 pts	Instructional ☐
0–3 pts	Frustrational ☐

A Biography

In 1892 a 13-year-old boy beat 25 men to win his first bike race. The boy was Marshall Taylor, and he would become one of the best racers of all time.

Just four years after winning his first race, Taylor became the first black man in the United States to race for money. By the time he was 20 years old, he was setting many records for speed. Sadly, he was not allowed to enter some races because of the color of his skin.

In the years that followed, Taylor raced all over the world. He won almost every race he entered. Millions of people came to see him, and he made friends everywhere he went. Taylor would stop racing in 1924 at the age of 32. But before he did, he broke every speed record there was to earn the title of the fastest bike racer in the world.

Passage 3C Oral—Nonfiction

A Biography

In 1892 *a* 13-year-old boy beat 25 men *to* win *his first* bike race. *The* boy *was* Marshall Taylor, *and he would become* one *of the best* racers *of all* time.

Just four years *after* winning *his first* race, Taylor became *the first black* man *in the* United States *to* race *for* money. *By the* time *he was* 20 years old, *he was* setting *many* records *for* speed. Sadly, *he was not* allowed *to* enter *some* races *because of the* color *of his* skin.

In the years *that* followed, Taylor raced *all over the* world. *He* won almost *every* race *he* entered. Millions *of* people *came to see him, and he made* friends everywhere *he went.* Taylor *would stop* racing *in* 1924 *at the* age *of* 32. *But before he did*, he broke *every* speed record *there was to* earn *the* title *of the* fastest bike racer *in the* world.

(150 words) (86 Dolch words) Number of Word Recognition Errors _____

Questions

L 1. _____ How old was Taylor when he won his first bike race? [13] (1 pt.)

L 2. _____ What was Taylor the first black man to do? [Race for money] (1 pt.)

V 3. _____ What is skin? [Outer covering of the human body] (3 pts.)

I 4. _____ What happened that would make you think Taylor was popular? [Millions of people came to see him, and he made friends everywhere he went.] (4 pts.)

L 5. _____ In what year did Taylor stop racing? [1924] (1 pt.)

Total # of points earned _____

Scoring Table for Oral Reading				
Total Points Earned	**# of Word Recognition Errors**			**Reading Level**
	0–8	**9–15**	**16+**	
7–10 pts	✓	*	–	Independent ☐
4–6 pts	*	*	–	Instructional ☐
0–3 pts	–	–	–	Frustrational ☐

Sleep

People of all ages need to sleep, but some need more sleep than others do. As people grow older, they need less sleep. Babies sleep about 15 hours a day, while adults need about 8 hours of sleep every night.

Sleep is very important because it will give the body and mind time to rest and prepare for the next day. During the early stages of sleep, the heart does not beat as fast and the brain slows down. If a person dreams while asleep, the heart begins beating faster and the brain goes back into action. At this stage of sleep, your eyes move back and forth very fast under your closed lids.

When people don't get enough sleep, they may be hard to get along with. They also may have trouble thinking and doing things. After five days with no sleep, people will start to see things that are not actually there.

Passage 3D Silent—Nonfiction

Sleep

People of all ages need to sleep, but some need more sleep than others do. As people grow older, they need less sleep. Babies sleep about 15 hours a day, while adults need about 8 hours of sleep every night.

Sleep is very important because it will give the body and mind time to rest and prepare for the next day. During the early stages of sleep, the heart does not beat as fast and the brain slows down. If a person dreams while asleep, the heart begins beating faster and the brain goes back into action. At this stage of sleep, your eyes move back and forth very fast under your closed lids.

When people don't get enough sleep, they may be hard to get along with. They also may have trouble thinking and doing things. After five days with no sleep, people will start to see things that are not actually there.

(154 words)

Questions

I 1. _____ From the passage, you can tell that children sleep somewhere between 8 hours and how many hours? [15] (4 pts.)

L 2. _____ Why is sleep important? [Because it will give the body and mind time to rest and prepare for the next day] (1 pt.)

L 3. _____ What happens to your eyes when you dream? [They move back and forth very fast under your closed lids.] (1 pt.)

L 4. _____ What is one thing that may happen to people when they don't get enough sleep? [They may be hard to get along with, they may have trouble thinking, or they may have trouble doing things.] (1 pt.)

V 5. _____ The reading passage says, "After five days with no sleep, people will start to see things that are not actually there." What does the word *actually* mean? [Really] (3 pts.)

Total # of points earned _____

Scoring Table for Silent Reading	
Total Points Earned	**Reading Level**
7–10 pts	Independent ☐
4–6 pts	Instructional ☐
0–3 pts	Frustrational ☐

A Feel for Music

Having a real feel for music, Cora loved to play the piano for friends and family. The problem was that she made mistakes because she never found enough time to sit down and practice.

One day, Mrs. Ruiz, the music teacher, announced that there was going to be a concert, and she wanted Cora to play a piece of music of her choice. Very excited, Cora decided to play "My Favorite Things."

Mrs. Ruiz called all of the children to her house to play their pieces a few days before the concert. To Cora's horror, Matt had decided to play "My Favorite Things" too. Matt played the piece perfectly, but he did not put any feeling into his music. However, all Cora could think was that he would play without any mistakes, while she would make mistakes and look silly.

The next day, Cora told Mrs. Ruiz that she did not want to be in the concert. The teacher said sadly, "You are a very good player because you feel the music, but this means little unless you believe in your talent and give it the time it requires."

Passage 4A Oral—Fiction

A Feel for Music

Having *a real feel for* music, Cora loved *to play the* piano *for* friends *and* family. *The* problem *was that she made* mistakes *because she never* found enough time *to sit down and* practice.

One day, Mrs. Ruiz, *the* music teacher, announced *that there was going to be a* concert, *and she* wanted Cora *to play a* piece *of* music *of her* choice. *Very* excited, Cora decided *to play* "*My* Favorite Things."

Mrs. Ruiz called *all of the* children *to her* house *to play their* pieces *a* few days *before the* concert. *To* Cora's horror, Matt *had* decided *to play* "My Favorite Things" *too*. Matt played *the* piece perfectly, *but he did not put any* feeling *into his* music. However, *all* Cora *could* think *was that he would play* without any mistakes, while *she would make* mistakes *and look* silly.

The next day, Cora told Mrs. Ruiz *that she did not want to be in the* concert. *The* teacher *said* sadly, "*You are a very good* player *because you* feel *the* music, *but this* means *little* unless *you* believe *in your* talent *and give it the* time *it* requires."

(189 words) (107 Dolch Words) Number of Word Recognition Errors _____

Questions

L 1. ____ Why did Cora make mistakes when she played? [Because she didn't practice enough] (1 pt.)

L 2. ____ What song did Cora choose to play at the concert? ["My Favorite Things"] (1 pt.)

L 3. ____ Where did the children go a few days before the concert to play their pieces? [To Mrs. Ruiz's house] (1 pt.)

V 4. ____ What does the word *horror* mean in this story? [Shock or disappointment] (3 pts.)

I 5. ____ Why did Cora decide not to be in the concert? [Because she was afraid of looking foolish if Matt played the song better than she did] (4 pts.)

Total # of points earned _____

Scoring Table for Oral Reading				
	# of Word Recognition Errors			
Total Points Earned	**0–11**	**12–18**	**19+**	**Reading Level**
7–10 pts	✓	*	–	Independent ☐
4–6 pts	*	*	–	Instructional ☐
0–3 pts	–	–	–	Frustrational ☐

The Bracelet

Mrs. Dell was delighted when her children gave her a very special present for her birthday. It was a beautiful gold bracelet with five charms, one charm from each of her five children. The clasp on the bracelet was a bit loose, but she planned to have that fixed just as soon as she could get around to it.

Not willing to take the bracelet off, Mrs. Dell wore it always, whether she was at work or doing the household chores. One night before she went to bed, she noticed that the bracelet was not on her wrist. Frantic, she looked for it everywhere, but she just couldn't find it. Feeling miserable, she told the children that she had lost their special gift.

Fifteen years later, all of Mrs. Dell's children were grown and out of the house, so she decided to sell it. The movers had just removed the last piece of furniture, the big sofa, when Mrs. Dell noticed something shiny on the floor. There was her lost bracelet, just like a special gift all over again.

© Macmillan/McGraw-Hill

Passage 4B Silent—Fiction

The Bracelet

Mrs. Dell was delighted when her children gave her a very special present for her birthday. It was a beautiful gold bracelet with five charms, one charm from each of her five children. The clasp on the bracelet was a bit loose, but she planned to have that fixed just as soon as she could get around to it.

Not willing to take the bracelet off, Mrs. Dell wore it always, whether she was at work or doing the household chores. One night before she went to bed, she noticed that the bracelet was not on her wrist. Frantic, she looked for it everywhere, but she just couldn't find it. Feeling miserable, she told the children that she had lost their special gift.

Fifteen years later, all of Mrs. Dell's children were grown and out of the house, so she decided to sell it. The movers had just removed the last piece of furniture, the big sofa, when Mrs. Dell noticed something shiny on the floor. There was her lost bracelet, just like a special gift all over again.

(180 words)

Questions

L 1. _____ For what occasion did Mrs. Dell's children give her the bracelet?
[Her birthday] (1 pt.)

L 2. _____ When did Mrs. Dell notice that the bracelet was missing? [One night before she went to bed] (1 pt.)

I 3. _____ What probably caused the bracelet to fall off of Mrs. Dell's wrist? [The loose clasp] (4 pts.)

V 4. _____ What does the word *frantic* mean in this story? [Very excited with worry or fear] (3 pts.)

L 5. _____ Where did Mrs. Dell eventually find her bracelet? [On the floor under where the big sofa had been] (1 pt.)

Total # of points earned _____

Scoring Table for Silent Reading	
Total Points Earned	**Reading Level**
7–10 pts	Independent ☐
4–6 pts	Instructional ☐
0–3 pts	Frustrational ☐

Gravity

The force that draws objects toward one another is called gravity. It is the earth's gravity that keeps the moon moving around it and holds the ocean waters against it.

Tides are the rise and fall of large bodies of water. They are caused by the gravity of the moon and the sun, which serves to pull on the waters of the earth. Even though the moon is much smaller than the sun, it has a stronger pull because it is much closer to the earth than the sun is.

When the moon is directly overhead, its gravity causes the waters of the earth to move toward it. As the water follows the moon, the oceans puff out in its direction, resulting in a high tide. When this happens, water rises and can come up onto the land for a short distance. A second bulge occurs on the opposite side of our planet because the earth is also being pulled toward the moon and away from the water on that side. As the moon moves farther away, the water drawn to it will fall back in a low tide.

Passage 4C Oral—Nonfiction

Gravity

The force *that* draws objects toward *one* another *is* called gravity. *It is the* earth's gravity *that* keeps *the* moon moving *around it and* holds *the* ocean waters against *it.*

Tides *are the* rise *and fall of* large bodies *of* water. *They are* caused *by the* gravity *of the* moon *and the* sun, *which* serves *to pull on the* waters *of the* earth. Even though *the* moon *is much* smaller than *the* sun, *it has a* stronger *pull because it is much* closer *to the* earth than *the* sun *is.*

When the moon *is* directly overhead, *its* gravity causes *the* waters *of the* earth *to* move toward *it. As the* water follows *the* moon, *the* oceans puff *out in its* direction, resulting *in a* high tide. *When this* happens, water rises *and can come up* onto *the* land *for a* short distance. *A* second bulge occurs *on the* opposite side *of our* planet *because the* earth *is* also being pulled toward *the* moon *and away from the* water *on that* side. *As the* moon moves farther *away, the* water drawn *to it will fall* back *in a* low tide.

(189 words) (102 Dolch words) Number of Word Recognition Errors _____

Questions

L 1. _____ What keeps the moon moving around the earth and holds the ocean waters against the earth? [Gravity] (1 pt.)

L 2. _____ Why does the moon have a greater pull on the earth's water than the sun does? [Because the moon is much closer to earth] (1 pt.)

L 3. _____ What causes a high tide? [Ocean waters puff out toward the moon when it is directly overhead.] (1 pt.)

V 4. _____ What is a *bulge*? [A part that swells out] (3 pts.)

I 5. _____ Why does the moon affect tides more than the sun does? [Because the moon is closer to Earth and has a stronger pull.] (4 pts.)

Total # of points earned _____

	Scoring Table for Oral Reading			
	# of Word Recognition Errors			
Total Points Earned	**0–11**	**12–18**	**19+**	**Reading Level**
7–10 pts	✓	*	–	Independent ☐
4–6 pts	*	*	–	Instructional ☐
0–3 pts	–	–	–	Frustrational ☐

A Biography of Sequoya

Born around 1765, Sequoya was a member of the Cherokee tribe. He was always fascinated by the white people's ability to communicate with one another by making marks on paper, which he would call "talking leaves." In 1809, he decided that the Cherokee should have a written language of their own. In spite of constant teasing by friends and family, Sequoya gave 12 years of his life to creating an alphabet for his people.

Sequoya found out that the Cherokee language was made up of a particular group of sounds. His alphabet gave a symbol for each of these sounds, resulting in 85 letters in all.

In 1821, Sequoya showed the leading men of the Cherokee Nation how his new alphabet worked. These wise men at once recognized the great worth of the alphabet and quickly adopted it for their people. In just a matter of months, thousands of Cherokee were able to read and write their own language for the first time. Because of Sequoya's vision, the Cherokee could now keep a written record of their great history to be handed down to generations to come.

Passage 4D Silent—Nonfiction

A Biography of Sequoya

Born around 1765, Sequoya was a member of the Cherokee tribe. He was always fascinated by the white people's ability to communicate with one another by making marks on paper, which he would call "talking leaves." In 1809, he decided that the Cherokee should have a written language of their own. In spite of constant teasing by friends and family, Sequoya gave 12 years of his life to creating an alphabet for his people.

Sequoya found out that the Cherokee language was made up of a particular group of sounds. His alphabet gave a symbol for each of these sounds, resulting in 85 letters in all.

In 1821, Sequoya showed the leading men of the Cherokee Nation how his new alphabet worked. These wise men at once recognized the great worth of the alphabet and quickly adopted it for their people. In just a matter of months, thousands of Cherokee were able to read and write their own language for the first time. Because of Sequoya's vision, the Cherokee could now keep a written record of their great history to be handed down to generations to come.

(187 words)

Questions

L 1. _____ What were "talking leaves"? [What Sequoya called the marks on paper used by white people to communicate with one another] (1 pt.)

L 2. _____ What did Sequoya spend 12 years of his life doing? [Creating an alphabet for his people] (1 pt.)

V 3. _____ What does the word *adopted* mean in this passage? [Accepted] (3pts.)

I 4. _____ How do you know that Sequoya's alphabet was easy to use? [In just a matter of months, thousands of Cherokee were able to read and write their own language for the first time.] (4 pts.)

L 5. _____ What did Sequoya's alphabet allow the Cherokee to do? [Keep a written record of their history to be handed down to generations to come] (1 pt.)

Total # of points earned _____

Scoring Table for Silent Reading	
Total Points Earned	**Reading Level**
7–10 pts	Independent ☐
4–6 pts	Instructional ☐
0–3 pts	Frustrational ☐

The Wolf and the Dog

A scrawny wolf was almost dead with hunger when he happened to meet a house dog who was passing by. "Cousin," said the dog, "your irregular life will soon be the ruin of you. Why don't you work steadily as I do, and get your food regularly given to you?"

"I would have no objection," said the wolf, "if I could only get a place."

"I will arrange that for you if you come with me to my master and share my work," said the dog.

So the wolf and dog went towards the town together. On the way there, the wolf noticed that the hair on a certain part of the dog's neck was very much worn away, so he asked him how that had come about.

"Oh," said the dog, "that is only the place where the collar is put on at night to keep me chained up. It does irritate the neck a bit, but you'll soon get used to it."

"Goodbye to you," said the wolf, "for it is better to be free and starve than be a fat slave."

Passage 5A Oral—Fiction

The Wolf and the Dog

A scrawny wolf was almost dead with hunger when he happened to meet a house dog who was passing by. "Cousin," said the dog, "your irregular life will soon be the ruin of you. Why don't you work steadily as I do, and get your food regularly given to you?"

"I would have no objection," said the wolf, "if I could only get a place."

"I will arrange that for you if you come with me to my master and share my work," said the dog.

So the wolf and dog went towards the town together. On the way there the wolf noticed that the hair on a certain part of the dog's neck was very much worn away, so he asked him how that had come about.

"Oh," said the dog, "that is only the place where the collar is put on at night to keep me chained up. It does irritate the neck a bit, but you'll soon get used to it."

"Goodbye to you," said the wolf, "for it is better to be free and starve than be a fat slave."

(184 Words) Number of Word Recognition Errors _____

Questions

L 1. _____ Why was the wolf almost dead? [Lack of food] (1 pt.)

I 2. _____ What did the dog do that would make you think he liked the wolf? [He offered to arrange for the wolf to work for his master.] (4 pts.)

L 3. _____ Why was the hair on the dog's neck worn away? [He had to wear a collar at night.] (1 pt.)

V 4. _____ What does the word *irritate* mean in this story? [Make sore] (3 pts.)

L 5. _____ Why does the wolf say goodbye to the dog? [Because he'd rather starve than be chained up] (1 pt.)

Total # of points earned _____

Scoring Table for Oral Reading				
	# of Word Recognition Errors			
Total Points Earned	**0–10**	**11–18**	**19+**	**Reading Level**
7–10 pts	✓	*	–	Independent ☐
4–6 pts	*	*	–	Instructional ☐
0–3 pts	–	–	–	Frustrational ☐

Tracy's Find

Life in Tracy's household became very challenging after her father lost his job. Now the entire family had to watch what they spent, and simple pleasures like buying new clothes or eating out were luxuries that Tracy rarely enjoyed.

With winter fast approaching and Tracy in desperate need of boots, she and her mother visited the used clothing store. Embarrassed and miserable, Tracy searched through the boots until she spied a pair in her size that weren't too worn. When she picked one up to try it on, she noticed something stuffed inside. She was stunned when she stuck in her hand and pulled out a little over $1000 in cash.

Thrilled, she raced over to her mother and said excitedly, "Mom, I found all this money in these boots! The person who gave the boots away won't miss it, so we can keep it, can't we?"

Tracy's mother didn't respond, but the sad and disappointed expression on her face spoke volumes. Ashamed of herself, Tracy knew what her mother expected of her, and she did not hesitate to do it.

Passage 5B Silent—Fiction

Tracy's Find

Life in Tracy's household became very challenging after her father lost his job. Now the entire family had to watch what they spent, and simple pleasures like buying new clothes or eating out were luxuries that Tracy rarely enjoyed.

With winter fast approaching and Tracy in desperate need of boots, she and her mother visited the used clothing store. Embarrassed and miserable, Tracy searched through the boots until she spied a pair in her size that weren't too worn. When she picked one up to try it on, she noticed something stuffed inside. She was stunned when she stuck in her hand and pulled out a little over $1000 in cash.

Thrilled, she raced over to her mother and said excitedly, "Mom, I found all this money in these boots! The person who gave the boots away won't miss it, so we can keep it, can't we?"

Tracy's mother didn't respond, but the sad and disappointed expression on her face spoke volumes. Ashamed of herself, Tracy knew what her mother expected of her, and she did not hesitate to do it.

(181 words)

Questions

L 1. _____ Why did life in Tracy's household become challenging? [Because her father lost his job] (1 pt.)

L 2. _____ Why was Tracy in the used clothing store? [She needed boots for winter.] (1 pt.)

V 3. _____ What does the word *stunned* mean in this story? [Amazed] (3 pts.)

L 4. _____ What did Tracy want to do with the money she found? [Keep it] (1 pt.)

I 5. _____ What did Tracy's mother expect her to do? [Return the money] (5 pts.)

Total # of points earned _____

Scoring Table for Silent Reading	
Total Points Earned	**Reading Level**
7–10 pts	Independent ☐
4–6 pts	Instructional ☐
0–3 pts	Frustrational ☐

Clouds

Throughout history, people have found clouds to be both interesting and beautiful. Clouds begin to form when warm, damp air is pushed up by cool, dry air. As the warm air rises, it begins to expand and cool. The cooling air is no longer able to hold all of the moisture in gas form that it was able to hold when it was warm. Eventually, tiny drops of water or ice crystals begin to form on bits of dust, taking the shape of a cloud. After the drops or ice crystals form, they can collide with each other and grow by joining together to such a large size that they fall to the ground as rain or snow.

There are four basic families of clouds, with each forming at a different distance above the earth. High clouds form above 20,000 feet, middle clouds appear between 6,500 feet and 20,000 feet, and low clouds appear below 6,500 feet. Finally, there are clouds that are moving upward while their bases are near the ground. These clouds with vertical development range from 1,600 feet to over 20,000 feet.

Passage 5C Oral—Nonfiction

Clouds

Throughout history, people have found clouds to be both interesting and beautiful. Clouds begin to form when warm, damp air is pushed up by cool, dry air. As the warm air rises, it begins to expand and cool. The cooling air is no longer able to hold all of the moisture in gas form that it was able to hold when it was warm. Eventually, tiny drops of water or ice crystals begin to form on bits of dust, taking the shape of a cloud. After the drops or ice crystals form, they can collide with each other and grow by joining together to such a large size that they fall to the ground as rain or snow.

There are four basic families of clouds, with each forming at a different distance above the earth. High clouds form above 20,000 feet, middle clouds appear between 6,500 feet and 20,000 feet, and low clouds appear below 6,500 feet. Finally, there are clouds that are moving upward while their bases are near the ground. These clouds with vertical development range from 1,600 feet to over 20,000 feet.

(185 words) Number of Word Recognition Errors _____

Questions

L 1. _____ What happens to the warm air as it rises? [It begins to expand and cool.] (1 pt.)

V 3. _____ What does the word *moisture* mean in this reading passage? [Wetness] (3 pts.)

L 2. _____ What makes the shape of a cloud? [Tiny drops of water or ice crystals forming on bits of dust] (1 pt.)

L 4. _____ At what distance above earth do middle clouds appear? [Between 6,500 feet and 20,000 feet] (1 pt.)

I 5. _____ Which family of clouds would produce the tallest clouds? [Clouds with vertical development] (4 pts.)

Total # of points earned _____

Scoring Table for Oral Reading				
	# of Word Recognition Errors			
Total Points Earned	**0–10**	**11–18**	**19+**	**Reading Level**
7–10 pts	✓	*	–	Independent ☐
4–6 pts	*	*	–	Instructional ☐
0–3 pts	–	–	–	Frustrational ☐

Deserts

Most people think of a desert as a wide, empty stretch of coarse sand and low dunes. Although some parts of large deserts do resemble this description, there are other regions that do not fit this picture.

To be a desert, a territory must have less than ten inches of rain a year. These dry areas are widely scattered over the earth, covering one-fifth of its land surface. The Sahara is the world's largest desert, stretching 3,200 miles across northern Africa and covering an area almost as large as the United States. The Sahara is the driest and hottest of all the world's deserts, creating one of the harshest environments on Earth.

You might be astonished to learn that only one-fifth of the entire area of the Sahara is covered with sand. If you travel through the Sahara, you'll see snow-capped mountains, such as the Tibesti, which are higher than 10,000 feet. There are also lakes such as Lake Chad, which is the size of the state of New Jersey. Also native to the Sahara are canyons, stony plains, and fifty oases, which are desert areas containing water.

Passage 5D Silent—Nonfiction

Deserts

Most people think of a desert as a wide, empty stretch of coarse sand and low dunes. Although some parts of large deserts do resemble this description, there are other regions that do not fit this picture.

To be a desert, a territory must have less than ten inches of rain a year. These dry areas are widely scattered over the earth, covering one-fifth of its land surface. The Sahara is the world's largest desert, stretching 3,200 miles across northern Africa and covering an area almost as large as the United States. The Sahara is the driest and hottest of all the world's deserts, creating one of the harshest environments on Earth.

You might be astonished to learn that only one-fifth of the entire area of the Sahara is covered with sand. If you travel through the Sahara, you'll see snow-capped mountains, such as the Tibesti, which are higher than 10,000 feet. There are also lakes such as Lake Chad, which is the size of the state of New Jersey. Also native to the Sahara are canyons, stony plains, and fifty oases, which are desert areas containing water.

(188 words)

Questions

V 1. _____ What does the word *resemble* mean in this reading passage? [Look like] (3 pts.)

L 2. _____ To be a desert, what must a territory have? [Less than ten inches of rain a year] (1 pt.)

L 3. _____ Where is the Sahara located? [Northern Africa] (1 pt.)

I 4. _____ What in the passage would make you think that relatively few people live in the Sahara? [It is the driest and hottest of all the world's deserts, creating one of the harshest environments on Earth.] (4 pts.)

L 5. _____ How much of the entire area of the Sahara is covered with sand? [One-fifth] (1 pt.)

Total # of points earned _____

Scoring Table for Silent Reading	
Total Points Earned	**Reading Level**
7–10 pts	Independent ☐
4–6 pts	Instructional ☐
0–3 pts	Frustrational ☐

Androcles and the Lion

A slave named Androcles once escaped from his master and fled to the forest. As he wandered about there, he came upon a lion moaning and groaning in acute pain. At first he turned to flee, but then he saw that the lion's paw was all swollen and bleeding due to the presence of a huge thorn. Androcles pulled out the thorn and bound up the paw, after which the lion licked the man's hand in appreciation and the two became fast friends.

Shortly afterwards both Androcles and the lion were captured, and the slave was sentenced to be thrown to the lion after the latter had not been fed for several days. The emperor and all his court came to see the spectacle, and Androcles was led out into the middle of the arena. Soon the ravenous lion was let loose and rushed roaring toward his victim. But as soon as he approached Androcles, he recognized his friend and licked his hand. The emperor, astounded at this, summoned Androcles to him. After hearing the slave's exceptional story, the emperor freed him and released the lion to his native forest.

Passage 6A Oral—Fiction

Androcles and the Lion

A slave named Androcles once escaped from his master and fled to the forest. As he wandered about there, he came upon a lion moaning and groaning in acute pain. At first he turned to flee, but then he saw that the lion's paw was all swollen and bleeding due to the presence of a huge thorn. Androcles pulled out the thorn and bound up the paw, after which the lion licked the man's hand in appreciation and the two became fast friends.

Shortly afterwards both Androcles and the lion were captured, and the slave was sentenced to be thrown to the lion after the latter had not been fed for several days. The emperor and all his court came to see the spectacle, and Androcles was led out into the middle of the arena. Soon the ravenous lion was let loose and rushed roaring toward his victim. But as soon as he approached Androcles, he recognized his friend and licked his hand. The emperor, astounded at this, summoned Androcles to him. After hearing the slave's exceptional story, the emperor freed him and released the lion to his native forest.

(190 words) Number of Word Recognition Errors _____

Questions

L 1. _____ Why was Androcles in the forest? [He fled there after escaping from his master.] (1 pt.)

I 2. _____ What in the story supports the idea that Androcles is both brave and considerate? [He tends to the wounded lion despite the danger.] (4 pts.)

L 3. _____ What was Androcles's sentence after he was captured? [He was to be thrown to the lion after it had not been fed for several days.] (1 pt.)

L 4. _____ Why didn't the lion attack Androcles? [Because he recognized the friend who had helped him in the forest] (1 pt.)

V 5. _____ What does the word *exceptional* mean in this story? [Extraordinary] (3 pts.)

Total # of points earned _____

	Scoring Table for Oral Reading			
	# of Word Recognition Errors			
Total Points Earned	**0–11**	**12–19**	**20+**	**Reading Level**
7–10 pts	✓	*	–	Independent ☐
4–6 pts	*	*	–	Instructional ☐
0–3 pts	–	–	–	Frustrational ☐

Morgan's Escape

After making her escape, Morgan glanced nervously around as she slowly moved into the deserted street. Hearing someone approaching from behind, she crouched behind some trash cans and peeked out to see the figure of a man. As he called her name, she recognized the familiar voice of Ben, someone she had once foolishly trusted. He had lost her trust by taking her to that awful place where a woman in a white coat had placed her on a cold table. Luckily, she had managed to escape and make a run for her life.

As Ben stepped closer to the spot where Morgan was hiding, she crouched down lower, hoping that he would not detect her. Frozen with fear, she reacted too late when Ben grabbed her.

Indignant and humiliated, Morgan struggled to be free, but Ben held her resolutely and said, "You shouldn't have run out of the veterinarian's office, you silly cat. Now let's go home so we can both get something to eat." At the mention of food, Morgan decided to forgive Ben and go quietly home with him.

Passage 6B Silent—Fiction

Morgan's Escape

After making her escape, Morgan glanced apprehensively around as she cautiously moved into the deserted street. Hearing someone approaching from behind, she crouched behind some trash cans and peeked out to see the figure of a man. As he called her name, she recognized the familiar voice of Ben, someone she had once foolishly trusted. He had betrayed her trust by taking her to that appalling place where a woman in a white coat had placed her on a cold table. Luckily, she had managed to escape and make a run for her life.

As Ben stepped closer to the spot where Morgan was hiding, she crouched down lower, hoping that he would not detect her. Frozen with fear, she reacted too late when Ben grabbed her.

Indignant and humiliated, Morgan struggled to be free, but Ben held her resolutely and said, "You shouldn't have run out of the veterinarian's office, you silly cat. Now let's go home so we can both get something to eat." At the mention of food, Morgan decided to forgive Ben and go quietly home with him.

(182 words)

Questions

L 1. _____ Where did Morgan hide when she heard someone approaching? [Behind some trash cans] (1 pt.)

L 2. _____ Who was looking for Morgan? [Ben] (1 pt.)

V 3. _____ What does the word *appalling* mean in this story? [Awful] (3 pts.)

I 4. _____ Who was the woman in the white coat? [The veterinarian] (4 pts.)

L 5. _____ Why did Morgan decide to go quietly home with Ben? [He mentioned food.] (1 pt.)

Total # of points earned _____

Scoring Table for Silent Reading	
Total Points Earned	**Reading Level**
7–10 pts	Independent ☐
4–6 pts	Instructional ☐
0–3 pts	Frustrational ☐

© Macmillan/McGraw-Hill

Comets

People have long been both awed and alarmed by comets flashing across the sky. To people of the past who didn't understand the movement of heavenly bodies, the ominous sight of a comet was often linked to terrible events such as wars or plagues. The earliest known record of a comet sighting was made in China around 1059 B.C. Since then, these regular visitors have been observed by astronomers like Edmond Halley, who first proved that comets return as they orbit the sun.

Comets, sometimes called "dirty snowballs," are lumps of dust and rock held together by ice. They orbit the sun in an oval path that brings them very close to it and swings them deep into space. As a dark, cold comet approaches the sun, it goes through a spectacular change. Usually, heated ice turns to water first and then evaporates to form a gas. However, when a comet gets close to the sun, the intense heat changes the surface ice directly into gases, which begin to glow. Fountains of dust and gas squirt out for millions of miles, forming a long tail that glows from reflected sunlight.

Passage 6C Oral—Nonfiction

Comets

People have long been both awed and alarmed by comets flashing across the sky. To people of the past who didn't understand the movement of heavenly bodies, the ominous sight of a comet was often linked to terrible events such as wars or plagues. The earliest known record of a comet sighting was made in China around 1059 B.C. Since then, these regular visitors have been observed by astronomers like Edmond Halley, who first proved that comets return as they orbit the sun.

Comets, sometimes called "dirty snowballs," are lumps of dust and rock held together by ice. They orbit the sun in an oval path that brings them very close to it and swings them deep into space. As a dark, cold comet approaches the sun, it goes through a spectacular change. Usually, heated ice turns to water and then evaporates. However, when a comet gets close to the sun, the intense heat changes the surface ice directly into gases, which begin to glow. Fountains of dust and gas squirt out for millions of miles, forming a long tail that glows from reflected sunlight.

(190 words) Number of Word Recognition Errors _____

Questions

V 1. _____ What does the word *ominous* mean in this reading passage? [Threatening or alarming] (3 pts.)

L 2. _____ Who first proved that comets return as they orbit the sun? [Edmond Halley] (1 pt.)

L 3. _____ What are comets made of? [Lumps of dust and rock held together by ice] (1 pt.)

L 4. _____ What does the intense heat of the sun do to the comet? [Changes the surface ice directly into gases, which begin to glow] (1 pt.)

I 5. _____ How does the comet change as it moves away from the sun in its orbit? [It grows cold once more and the ice refreezes.] (4 pts.)

Total # of points earned _____

Scoring Table for Oral Reading				
	# of Word Recognition Errors			
Total Points Earned	**0–11**	**12–19**	**20+**	**Reading Level**
7–10 pts	✓	*	–	Independent ☐
4–6 pts	*	*	–	Instructional ☐
0–3 pts	–	–	–	Frustrational ☐

Sybil's Ride

Everyone has heard of Paul Revere's ride to warn a sleeping countryside that the British were coming. About two years later, there was another essential ride—this time made by a girl named Sybil Ludington.

The eldest child of Colonel Henry Ludington, Sybil was with her family in New York on the night of April 26, 1777, when a messenger knocked on the door. He related that the British were burning the town of Danbury, Connecticut, only 25 miles away. With his men scattered over a wide area, Colonel Ludington had to alert them and organize his troops to fend off the British raid. Not being able to do both, he consented to let Sybil ride to summon the men.

It was raining hard that night, but Sybil rode her horse over 40 miles on dark, unmarked roads to notify the men to gather at her home. When, soaked and exhausted, she returned home, most of the soldiers were ready to march. The men whom she gathered arrived in time to drive the British back to their ships in Long Island Sound. After the battle, General George Washington congratulated Sybil for her heroism.

Passage 6D Silent—Nonfiction

Sybil's Ride

Everyone has heard of Paul Revere's ride to warn a sleeping countryside that the British were coming. About two years later, there was another essential ride—this time made by a girl named Sybil Ludington.

The eldest child of Colonel Henry Ludington, Sybil was with her family in New York on the night of April 26, 1777, when a messenger knocked on the door. He related that the British were burning the town of Danbury, Connecticut, only 25 miles away. With his men scattered over a wide area, Colonel Ludington had to alert them and organize his troops to fend off the British raid. Not being able to do both, he consented to let Sybil ride to summon the men.

It was raining hard that night, but Sybil rode her horse over 40 miles on dark, unmarked roads to notify the men to gather at her home. When, soaked and exhausted, she returned home, most of the soldiers were ready to march. The men whom she gathered arrived in time to drive the British back to their ships in Long Island Sound. After the battle, General George Washington congratulated Sybil for her heroism.

(193 words)

Questions

V 1. ____ What does the word *essential* mean in this reading passage? [Very important] (3 pts.)

L 2. ____ What did the messenger tell Sybil and her family? [The British were burning the town of Danbury, Connecticut] (1 pt.)

L 3. ____ What did Colonel Ludington consent to let Sybil do? [Ride to summon the men] (1 pt.)

I 4. ____ How do you know that Sybil was a skillful horsewoman? [Because she successfully rode over 40 miles in the rain and dark over unmarked roads] (4 pts.)

L 5. ____ What did the men whom Sybil gathered succeed in doing? [Driving the British back to their ships in Long Island Sound] (1 pt.)

Total # of points earned _____

Scoring Table for Silent Reading	
Total Points Earned	**Reading Level**
7–10 pts	Independent ☐
4–6 pts	Instructional ☐
0–3 pts	Frustrational ☐

© Macmillan/McGraw-Hill

Informal Reading Inventory Record

Graded Word Lists

	Grade Level	Date Administered
Independent		
Instructional		
Frustrational		

Oral Reading Passage

	Grade Level	Date Administered
Independent		
Instructional		
Frustrational		

Silent Reading Passage

	Grade Level	Date Administered
Independent		
Instructional		
Frustrational		

Comments:

Contents

How to Use the Placement Tests

The primary purpose of the Placement Tests for K–6 is to help you determine the instructional levels of your students. The Placement Tests are intended to be group administered (except in Kindergarten, where the test is individually administered). We recommend administering the Placement Test at or near the beginning of the year.

There is one Placement Test for each grade. The Kindergarten Placement measures Concepts of Print, Letter Recognition, Phonics, Word Recognition, and Comprehension. The tests for grades 1–6 measure Phonics in grades 1–2, Word Recognition in grades 1–3, and Vocabulary Strategies and Reading Comprehension in all grades.

The subscores from the specific skills tested will help you place students in the program for approaching, on level, and beyond level instruction. More detailed information about individual students may be gathered through the use of the Informal Reading Inventory, or the diagnostic instruments previously explained in this book.

Once a student has been placed for instruction, the teacher should observe the student closely for the next few weeks and make any necessary adjustments in placement. In addition, assessments should be conducted periodically throughout the year to monitor each student's progress and help adapt instruction to meet the needs of students.

Administering Tests

When you are ready to administer a Placement Test, explain to students that the test will help you find the best reading level for them so that they can enjoy reading and build their reading skills. Make sure students are sitting in a comfortable setting with minimal distractions, and encourage them to do their best on the test.

In order to administer the test efficiently and make the directions understandable, you should be familiar with the directions and the test items before the test is given. During the administration, monitor students closely to make sure that each student is following the directions, is on the correct item, and is marking the test form correctly.

To administer a Placement Test:

- Turn to the grade-level Placement Test section of this book to find the grade-level Placement Test and specific directions for administration and scoring.
- Make a copy of the grade-level Placement Test for each student. Have students write their names and the date on the front cover of the test.
- Tell students which part or parts of the test they will work on and how much time they will need to complete each part.

Placement Test

Kindergarten

The Kindergarten Placement Test is designed to be administered individually. It is intended to be administered at or near the beginning of the year, but it may be used at any time during the school year when additional diagnostic information is needed, or when you receive new entrants into your classroom.

The kindergarten test has six parts. Each part will take 5–10 minutes to administer. The entire test will take a total of about 35 minutes to complete. The chart below shows the sections of the test, the number of test questions, or items, in each section, and the estimated amount of time required for administering each part. You may administer the entire test in several sessions, or you may choose to administer only some parts of the test.

Section	No. of Items	Estimated Time
Concepts of Print	5	5 minutes
Letter Recognition	5	5 minutes
Phonics	10	10 minutes
Word Recognition	4	5 minutes
Comprehension	6	10 minutes
Total	30	35 minutes

Plan to sit with one child for 10 to 15 minutes at a time. Try to sit away from other children so the child taking the test will not be distracted. If the child is unable to answer questions or becomes confused or upset at any time during the test, discontinue the assessment and try it again at a later time.

Directions for Administering the Test

To administer the Kindergarten Placement Test, make a copy of each part of the test that you plan to give. For all parts except Concepts of Print, give the child a pencil, crayon, or marker for marking answers. Also, make a copy of the Student Test Results Chart on page 138. The Student Test Results Chart may be used to keep a record of each child's performance on the test.

For each part of the test, read aloud the directions printed in italics below.

Concepts of Print

For this part of the assessment, choose a storybook with illustrations on top of the page and several lines of text at the bottom of the page. Then read the questions below. Record the child's responses by circling or checking each question correctly.

We're going to talk about how stories are read. I'm going to ask you some questions. (Hand the book to the child upside-down.)

1. *If I am going to read this story, how should I hold this book?* (Child should hold the book right-side up.)

(Open the book to the first page.)

2. *Where should I begin to read? Point to the place where I should start reading.* (Child should point to the first word on the page.)

3. *Show me a sentence. Point to the place where the sentence begins and ends.* (Child should identify a sentence's beginning and ending, indicating left-to-right progression.)

4. *Show me a word. What comes before and after the word?* (Child should point to a word and explain that a space comes before and after each word.)

5. *Suppose I am reading this story. When I get to the end of the page, what should I do next?* (Child should explain that you would turn to the next page and continue reading at the top left of where the words begin.)

Letter Recognition

For this part of the test, give the child a copy of the Letter Recognition page (page 2).

1. *Put your finger on the star. Look at the letters. Circle the lowercase __d__.*

2. *Put your finger on the moon. Look at the letters. Circle the lowercase __a__.*

3. *Put your finger on the sun. Look at the letters. Circle the capital __B__.*

4. *Put your finger on the circle. Look at the letters. Circle the lowercase* __u__.

5. *Put your finger on the heart. Look at the letters. Circle the capital* __R__.

Phonics

Give the child the Phonics pages of the test (pages 3 and 4).

Listen carefully to the beginning sound of each word I say. Then draw a circle around the letter that stands for that sound.

1. *Put your finger on the star at the top of the page. Look at the letters in the row. The word is* **nose**. *Draw a circle around the letter that stands for the first sound in* **nose**.

2. *Put your finger on the moon. Look at the letters in the row. The word is* **red**. *Draw a circle around the letter that stands for the first sound in* **red**.

3. *Put your finger on the sun. Look at the letters in the row. The word is* **pan**. *Draw a circle around the letter that stands for the first sound in* **pan**.

4. *Put your finger on the circle. Look at the letters in the row. The word is* **top**. *Draw a circle around the letter that stands for the first sound in* **top**.

5. *Put your finger on the heart. Look at the letters in a row. The word is* **bike**. *Draw a circle around the letter that stands for the first sound in* **bike**.

Have child look at page 4.

6. *Put your finger on the star at the top of the page. Look at the letters in the row. The word is* **six**. *Draw a circle around the letter that stands for the first sound in* **six**.

7. *Put your finger on the moon. Look at the letters in the row. The word is* **dog**. *Draw a circle around the letter that stands for the first sound in* **dog**.

8. *Put your finger on the sun. Look at the letters in the row. The word is* **at**. *Draw a circle around the letter that stands for the first sound in* **at**.

9. *Put your finger on the circle. Look at the letters in the row. The word is* **mop**. *Draw a circle around the letter that stands for the first sound in* **mop**.

10. *Put your finger on the heart. Look at the letters in the row. The word is* **lap**. *Draw a circle around the letter that stands for the first sound in* **lap**.

Word Recognition

This part of the test is about recognizing words. For each question, I will read a word aloud. You will look at the words in the row and find the word that I say. Mark your answer by drawing a circle around the word. Now we will begin. Listen carefully.

Have children point to the picture at the beginning of each row. Then read the word. Pause after each question to let children mark their answers.

1. *Point to the star. Look at the words in the row. Circle the word **can**.*

2. *Point to the moon. Look at the words in the row. Circle the word **the**.*

3. *Point to the sun. Look at the words in the row. Circle the word **we**.*

4. *Point to the circle. Look at the words in the row. Circle the word **I**.*

Comprehension

Give the child a copy of the Comprehension section of the test (pages 6–8). Read the story and the questions aloud. The child will answer the question by marking the answers.

Now I am going to read you a story. Listen to the story. Then I will ask you some questions. Here is the story.

The Amazing Fish

One day, a fisherman caught an amazing fish with his fishing pole. The fish asked to be let go. "I will grant you three wishes if you let me go," the fish said.

"Very well, said the fisherman. "I wish to be a king."

The fish granted the fisherman's first wish, but the fisherman was not happy.

"I wish for a castle," said the fisherman. So the fish granted the fisherman's second wish, but the fisherman was not happy.

"I wish for a bigger castle," said the fisherman. "I want one that reaches up to the sun!"

"That is not possible," said the fish. "Wish again."

The fisherman became very angry and stomped his foot. "Oh, how I wish I had never met you!" he screamed.

So the fish granted the fisherman's last wish. In an instant, the fisherman was no longer a king with a castle. He was a fisherman fishing in the sea.

Now I will read some questions.

Have the child look at page 6.

1. *Point to the star. Look at the pictures. Which picture shows what the fisherman wished for first? Circle the picture.*

2. *Point to the sun. Look at the pictures. Which picture shows what happened to the fisherman at the end of the story? Circle the picture.*

Have the child look at page 7.

3. *Point to the circle. Look at the pictures. Which picture shows what the fisherman wanted his castle to reach up to? Circle the picture.*

4. *Point to the triangle. Look at the pictures. Which picture shows something the fisherman used to catch fish? Circle the picture.*

Have the child look at page 8.

5. *Point to the moon. Look at the pictures. Which picture shows something that could **not** really happen? Circle the picture.*

6. *Point to the square. Look at the pictures. Which picture shows what will happen to the fisherman next? Circle the picture.*

Directions for Scoring the Test

The Kindergarten Placement Test is designed to be scored by each section. On page 137, you will find the Answer Key for this test. It lists the correct response for each question and, in the chart at the bottom, lists the skills measured by each test item. On page 138, you will find a Student Test Results Chart for this test. Make a copy of the chart for each child and use it to record the child's results on each part of the test.

Using the Answer Key, score the tests by marking each item correct or incorrect. Then:
• add up the number of questions answered correctly in each section;
• record the number correct in the space provided on the Student Test Results Chart;
• add the scores to determine the total test score.

To find the percentage score for each section, refer to the Scoring Chart on pages 254–255.

Interpreting Test Results

At the beginning of Kindergarten, children's test results will vary widely. Some children, for example, may recognize all the letters of the alphabet while others cannot recognize any letters. Use the results of the test to help plan your instruction for each child.

Children who score between 80% and 90% correct in each section are ready for on level instruction. Children who score 90% or higher in each section should receive some beyond level instruction. Children who score lower than 80% may need some approaching level instruction.

Use the scores on each section of the test to help make specific instructional plans for each child. For example, a child who scores 80% or higher in other sections but only 40% in Phonics would benefit from additional instruction that emphasizes sound-symbol connections. You may also want to refer to the Tested Skills Chart below the Answer Key to identify the skills measured by those items the child answered incorrectly.

For those children whose scores do not clearly define their areas of weaknesses and strengths, you may need to administer additional assessments. Administer a diagnostic assessment for those students who are significantly below grade level. See page 13 for reference. For children who seem to be significantly above grade level, you may want to administer the Placement Test for Grade 1 to collect additional information.

Placement Assessment • Grade K

Kindergarten Placement Test
Answer Key

Concepts of Print
(Answers are listed on page 132.)

Letter Recognition
1. d
2. a
3. B
4. u
5. R

Word Recognition
1. can
2. the
3. we
4. I

Phonics
1. n
2. r
3. p
4. t
5. b
6. s
7. d
8. a
9. m
10. l

Comprehension
1. 1st picture
2. 2nd picture
3. 3rd picture
4. 1st picture
5. 1st picture
6. 2nd picture

Tested Skills	Item Numbers
Concepts of Print	1–5
Letter Recognition Identify Capital and Lowercase letters	1–5
Phonics Beginning Sounds	1–10
Word Recognition Recognize High-Frequency Words	1–4
Comprehension Sequence Match Pictures to the Story	1, 2, 6 3, 4, 5

Name _____ Date _____

Grade _____

Student Test Results Chart
Kindergarten

Test Section	Number Correct	% Score	Notes
Concepts of Print	/5		
Letter Recognition	/10		
Phonics	/10		
Word Recognition	/4		
Comprehension	/6		

Additional Assessments Indicated:

_____

_____

Placement/Instructional Decisions:

_____

_____

Student's Name _____ Date _____

Teacher's Name _____ Grade _____

Placement Test
Kindergarten

Letter Recognition

1.   m   d   p

2.   a   s   X

3.   B   n   H

4.   E   q   u

5.   m   r   R

Name _____ Date _____

Phonics

1.

n   k   p

2.

a   r   l

3.

p   d   e

4.

b   f   t

5.

g   b   z

Phonics

6.

s   m   o

7.

x   d   u

8.

c   h   a

9.

m   q   I

10.

b   l   k

Name _____ Date _____

Word Recognition

1.

   go   my   can

2.

   are   the   to

3.

   we   and   have

4.

   I   she   that

Comprehension

1.

2.

Comprehension

3.

4.

 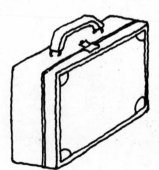 

Comprehension

5.

6.

Placement Test
Grade 1

The Grade 1 Placement Test has four sections and will take about 45 minutes to complete. The chart below shows the sections of the test, the number of test questions, or items, in each section, and the estimated amount of time required for administering each part. You may administer the entire test in several sessions, or you may choose to administer only some parts of the test.

Section	No. of Items	Estimated Time
Phonics	15	15 minutes
Word Recognition	10	10 minutes
Vocabulary	7	10 minutes
Comprehension	8	10 minutes
Total	40	45 minutes

Directions for Administering the Test

To begin the administration, have children turn to the Phonics section on the first page of the test (page 2). Read aloud the directions printed in italics below.

Phonics

In this part of the test, I will say the name of the picture. You will find the word that names the picture. Draw a circle around the word. Let's do the sample question first.

Sample (Hold up page 2 and point to the sample question.) *Look at the picture in the box at the top of the page. It is a picture of a rug. Look at the three words in the row next to the picture. Find the word rug. Draw a circle around the word rug.* (Check to see that children know what to do. Then have a child provide the correct answer.) *Yes, the word in the middle is rug: r-u-g. You should have drawn a circle around the middle word. Does anyone have any questions?* Pause and answer all questions.

Now we will continue in the same way. I will say the name of each picture. Circle the word that names the picture. Circle only one word in each row. Listen carefully.

Read the item number and the name of the picture. Pause after each question to let children mark their answers. Then have children move down to the next row.

  1. pot   **2.** bed   **3.** hat   **4.** cape   **5.** cub

Have children turn to the next page.
  6. bike   **7.** ham   **8.** lane   **9.** jog   **10.** pack

Have children turn to the next page.
11. ship   **12.** frog   **13.** doll   **14.** bank   **15.** chick

d Recognition section on page 5.

recognizing words. For each question, I will read a word
ree words in a row. Mark your answer by drawing a
s do the sample question first.

d point to the sample question.) *Look at the three words in
word that I say. The word is <u>and</u>.* (Check to see that the
Then have a child provide the correct answer.) *Yes, the first
uld have circled the first word. Does anyone have any*

tions.

words. *Find the word I say in each row. Draw a circle
e will begin. Listen carefully.*

e picture at the beginning of each row. Then read the word.
n to let children mark their answers.

ook at the words beside the star. Circle the word **me**.

2. Circle the word **with**.

3. *Point to the sun. Circle the word* **has**.

4. *Point to the circle. Circle the word* **are**.

5. *Point to the heart. Circle the word* **your**.

Have children turn to the next page.

6. *Point to the star at the top of the page. Circle the word* **see**.

7. *Point to the moon. Circle the word* **from**.

8. *Point to the sun. Circle the word* **away**.

9. *Point to the circle. Circle the word* **make**.

10. *Point to the heart. Circle the word* **but**.

Vocabulary

Have children turn to the Vocabulary section on the next page of the test (page 7). Hold up the page and point to the sample question at the top of the page. If children are not used to filling in answer bubbles, you may want to demonstrate on the chalkboard.

Sample. *Point to the row marked S. The sentence has a word missing. The missing word is one of the two words below the sentence. Find the word that belongs in the sentence and fill in the circle next to the word.* (Check to see that children know what to do. Then have a child provide a correct answer.) *Yes, choice b is the correct answer. The sentence should say, "The cat runs up the tree." You should have marked choice b. Does anyone have any questions?*

Answer children's questions. Then have children complete questions 1–3. When children are ready, have them look at the picture in the box.

Sample. *Look at the picture in the box marked S. Next to the picture is a sentence that tells about the picture. The sentence has a word missing. Choose the word that best fits in the sentence. Fill in the circle beside the word.* (Check to see that children know what to do. Then have a have a child provide the correct answer.) *Yes, choice b is the correct answer. The picture shows a baby. The sentence should say, "The baby cries." You should have marked choice b. Does anyone have any questions?*

Answer children's questions. Then have children turn to the next page and answer questions 4–7.

Comprehension

Have children turn to the Comprehension section of the test (page 9). There are two reading passages in this section. You will read the passages and the questions aloud. Children will answer the questions by marking pictures.

Now I am going to read you some stories. Listen to the first story. Then I will ask you some questions. Here is the story.

Have you ever seen a real bear? Most bears live in the mountains or the forest. Bears like to eat many different foods. They eat lots of nuts and berries. Some bears catch and eat fish from the rivers.

One of the bear's favorite foods is honey, which is made by bees. The bear finds a beehive and takes the honey.

All through the summer, bears eat a lot and get very big. When fall comes, the weather gets colder. When the leaves fall off the trees, the bear knows that winter will come soon. The bear finds a good place to go for winter, such as a cave or a hole in the ground. The bear climbs in and goes to sleep for the winter. In the spring, the bear will wake up and start eating again.

Now I will read some questions.

1. *Point to the star at the top of the page. Look at the pictures. What is the story mostly about? Fill in the circle under the picture that shows what the story is mostly about.*

2. *Point to the moon. Which picture shows where a bear gets honey? Fill in the circle under the picture that shows where the bear gets honey.*

3. *Point to the sun. Which picture shows how the bear knows when winter is coming? Fill in the circle under the picture that shows how the bear knows that winter is coming.*

4. *Point to the heart. Which picture shows where a bear likes to sleep for the winter? Fill in the circle under the picture that shows where a bear likes to sleep.*

Have children turn to the next page (page 10).

Now I am going to read another story. Listen carefully. Here is the story.

Working with Mom

Maya and Sam were excited about spending the day at the flower shop with their moms. Maya and Sam were best friends. Their families lived in the same apartment building, and their moms worked together in the same flower shop.

On Saturday morning, the four of them rode the bus together to the shop. When they got there, Maya's mom opened the door with a key. When the door opened, a little bell jingled.

"That bell will let us know when someone comes to buy something," said Sam's mom.

A minute later, the bell jingled. The first customer walked in.

"Hello, may I help you?" asked Maya's mom.

The man told them he would like a bouquet of fresh flowers.

"We'll make that for you, and it will be beautiful," said Maya's mom. "We have lots of help today."

Sam and Maya helped their moms choose the flowers. Sam's mom snipped the stems and put everything into a vase. "It's so pretty," said Maya.

The man was happy, too. "I think you should let these two come to work with you more often!" he said, smiling at Maya and Sam.

Maya and Sam were happy with the work they had done.

Now I will read some questions.

5. *Point to the star at the top of the page. Look at the pictures. Which picture shows what this story is mostly about? Fill in the circle under the picture.*

6. *Point to the moon. Which picture shows how Maya and Sam and their moms got to work? Fill in the circle under the picture that shows how they got to work.*

7. *Point to the sun. Which picture shows something that happens at the beginning of the story? Fill in the circle under the picture that shows something that happens at the beginning of the story.*

8. *Point to the heart. Which picture best shows how the two families feel about each other? Fill in the circle under the picture that best shows how the two families feel about each other.*

Directions for Scoring the Test

The Grade 1 Placement Test can be scored by section or by total test. On page 154, you will find the Answer Key for this test. It lists the correct response for each question and, in the chart at the bottom, lists the skill measured by each test item. On page 155, you will find a Student Test Results Chart for this test. Make a copy of the chart for each student and use it to record the student's results on each part of the test.

Using the Answer Key, score the tests by marking each item correct or incorrect. Then:
• add up the number of questions answered correctly in each section;
• record the number correct in the space provided on the Student Test Results Chart;
• add the scores to determine the total test score.
To find the percentage score for each section and the total test, refer to the Scoring Chart on pages 254–255.

Interpreting Test Results

At the beginning of Grade 1, children who achieve a total test score of 80%–90% should be given on level instruction. Children who score 90% or higher should receive beyond level instruction. Children who score lower than 80% should receive approaching level instruction.

Use the scores on each section of the test (Phonics, Word Recognition, Vocabulary, and Comprehension) to help make specific instructional plans for each child. For example, a child who scores 80% or higher in three sections but only 60% in Vocabulary would benefit from additional instruction that emphasizes vocabulary development. You may want to refer to the Tested Skills Chart below the Answer Key to identify the skills measured by those items the child answered incorrectly.

For those children whose scores do not clearly define their areas of weaknesses and strengths, you may need to administer additional assessments. Administer a diagnostic assessment for those students who are significantly below grade level. See page 13 for reference. For children who seem to be significantly above grade level, you may want to administer the Placement Test for Grade 2 to collect additional information.

Grade 1 Placement Test
Answer Key

Phonics
1. pot
2. bed
3. hat
4. cape
5. cub
6. bike
7. ham
8. lane
9. jog
10. pack
11. ship
12. frog
13. doll
14. bank
15. chick

Word Recognition
1. me
2. with
3. has
4. are
5. your
6. see
7. from
8. away
9. make
10. but

Vocabulary
1. b
2. a
3. a
4. c
5. c
6. a
7. c

Comprehension
1. c
2. b
3. a
4. c
5. c
6. a
7. a
8. a

Tested Skills	Item Numbers
Phonics	
Short Vowels	1, 2, 3, 5, 7, 9
Long Vowels	4, 6, 8
Consonant Blends and Digraphs	10–15
Word Recognition	
Recognize High-Frequency Words	1–10
Vocabulary	
Inflectional Endings	1–3
Context Clues	4–7
Comprehension	
Main Idea and Supporting Details	1–4
Analyze Character and Plot	5–8

Name _____ Date _____

Grade _____

Student Test Results Chart
Grade 1

Test Section	Number Correct	% Score	Notes
Phonics	/15		
Word Recognition	/10		
Vocabulary	/7		
Comprehension	/8		
Total	/40		

Additional Assessments Indicated:

_____

_____

Placement/Instructional Decisions:

_____

_____

Student's Name _____ Date _____

Teacher's Name _____ Grade _____

Placement Test
Grade 1

Name _____ Date _____

Phonics

S.		rag	rug	rig
1.		pot	pet	pit
2.		bud	bed	bad
3.		hit	hat	hut
4.		cope	cape	cane
5.		cab	cob	cub

© Macmillan/McGraw-Hill

Phonics

6.    bike   bit   bin

7.    him   hum   ham

8. 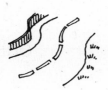   lane   land   line

9.    jog   jig   jug

10.    pick   peck   pack

Phonics

11.

ship   chip   slip

12.

fog   flag   frog

13.

dog   dock   doll

14.

bang   bank   band

15.

trick   slick   chick

© Macmillan/McGraw-Hill

Name _____ Date _____

Word Recognition

S.		and	the	as
1.		my	mom	me
2.		we	walk	with
3.		has	his	her
4.		at	are	and
5.		yes	you	your

Name _____ Date _____

Word Recognition

6.	see	saw	stop
7.	four	from	for
8.	am	are	away
9.	may	must	make
10.	be	but	big

Vocabulary

S. The cat _____ up a tree.

Ⓐ run   Ⓑ runs

1. They _____ with the puppy.

Ⓐ plays   Ⓑ played

2. Mom _____ at her baby.

Ⓐ looks   Ⓑ look

3. We _____ our school.

Ⓐ see   Ⓑ sees

S. The _____ cries.

Ⓐ bug   Ⓑ baby

Vocabulary

4. The girl's pet is a _____.

   Ⓐ cat   Ⓑ fish   Ⓒ dog

5. She _____ her dog.

   Ⓐ sings   Ⓑ makes   Ⓒ walks

6. The _____ is in his cave.

   Ⓐ bear   Ⓑ bat   Ⓒ rabbit

7. The bear _____ in his cave.

   Ⓐ runs   Ⓑ jumps   Ⓒ sleeps

Comprehension

1.

Ⓐ   Ⓑ   Ⓒ

2.

Ⓐ   Ⓑ   Ⓒ

3.

Ⓐ   Ⓑ   Ⓒ

4.

Ⓐ   Ⓑ   Ⓒ

Name _____ Date _____

Comprehension

5. ⭐

 (A)  (B)  (C)

6. 🌙

 (A)  (B)  (C)

7. ☀️

 (A)  (B)  (C)

8. ♡

 (A)  (B)  (C)

Placement Test
Grade 2

The Grade 2 Placement Test has four sections and will take about 60 minutes to complete. The chart below shows the sections of the test, the number of test questions, or items, in each section, and the estimated amount of time required for administering each part. You may administer the entire test in several sessions, or you may choose to administer only some parts of the test.

Section	No. of Items	Estimated Time
Phonics	20	20 minutes
Word Recognition	10	10 minutes
Vocabulary	10	10 minutes
Comprehension	10	20 minutes
Total	50	60 minutes

Directions for Administering the Test

To begin the administration, have children turn to the Phonics section on the first page of the test (page 2). Read aloud the directions printed in italics below.

Phonics

Point to the directions at the top of the page. Follow along as I read them aloud.

Look at the underlined letter in the word r<u>a</u>n. Now read the words in a row. Fill in the circle beside the word that has the same sound as the underlined letter in r<u>a</u>n. (Check to see that children know what to do. Then have a child provide the correct answer.) *Yes, the word d<u>a</u>d has the same vowel sound as the word r<u>a</u>n. You should have filled in the circle for choice <u>c</u>, d<u>a</u>d. Does anyone have any questions?*

Pause and answer any questions.

Now you will continue in the same way. There are 20 questions in this part. Fill in the circle beside the answer to each question. When you have finished question 20, look up at me.

Word Recognition

When the children are ready have them turn to the Word Recognition section of the test (page 5).

This part is about recognizing words. For each question, I will read a word aloud. You will look at four words in a row and find the word I say. Mark your answer by filling in the circle beside the word. Let's do the sample first.

Sample *Look at the four words in the box marked S. Find the word that I say. The word is <u>could</u>.* (Check to see if the children know what to do. Then have a child provide the correct answer.) *Yes, choice <u>a</u> is the correct answer. You should have marked circle <u>a</u>. Does anyone have any questions?*

Pause and answer all the questions.

Now, I will say some more words. Find the word I say in each row. Then mark your answer. Now we will begin. Listen carefully. Read the item number and the question. Pause after each question to let students mark their answers.

1. *Find the word **find**. Mark your answer. The word is **find**.*

2. *Find the word **many**. Mark your answer.*

3. *Find the word **together**. Mark your answer.*

4. *Find the word **sleep**. Mark your answer.*

5. *Find the word **pull**. Mark your answer.*

6. *Find the word **right**. Mark your answer.*

7. *Find the word **found**. Mark your answer.*

8. *Find the word **call**. Mark your answer.*

9. *Find the word **never**. Mark your answer*

10. *Find the word **would**. Mark your answer.*

Vocabulary

Have children turn to Vocabulary section on the next page of the test (page 6). In this part of the test, read aloud each set of directions and the sample directions. Have children answer questions 1–10 independently.

This part of the test is about vocabulary. Look at part A. Follow along as I read the directions:

A. *Read each sentence. Find the meaning of the underlined word. Mark your answer. Let's do the sample question.*

Sample. *Read the sentence in the box marked S. Find the meaning of the underlined word.* (Check to see that children know what to do. Then have a child provide the correct answer.) *Yes, choice **a** is the correct answer. The word protect means "guard." You should have marked circle **a**. Does anyone have any questions?*

Answer children's questions. Then have children complete questions 1–3. When children are ready, have them turn to the next page and continue with the next part.

Look at part B. Follow along as I read the directions:

B. *Look at the underlined word. Find the word that means the same as the underlined word. Mark your answer. Let's do the sample question.*

Sample *Find the word that means the same as the underlined word.* (Check to see that children know what to do. Then have a child provide the correct answer.) *Yes, choice b is the correct answer. The word <u>record</u> means the same as <u>write</u>. You should have marked circle <u>b</u>. Does anyone have any questions?*

Answer children's questions. Then have children complete questions 4–5. When children are ready, have them continue with the next part.

Look at part C. Follow along as I read the directions:

C. *Look at the underlined word. Find the word that means the opposite of the underlined word. Mark your answer. Let's do the sample question.*

Sample. *Find the word that means the same as the underlined word.* (Check to see what children know what to do. Then have a child provide the correct answer.) *Yes, choice d is the correct answer. The word <u>sick</u> means the opposite of <u>healthy</u>. You should have marked circle <u>d</u>. Does anyone have any questions?*

Answer children's questions. Then have children complete questions 6–7. When children are ready, have them turn to the next page and continue with the next part.

Look at part D. Follow along as I read the directions:

D. *Read the words in each row. Choose the word that is made of two small words. Mark your answer. Let's do the sample question first.*

Sample. *Find the word that is made of two small words.* (Check to see that children know what to do. Then have a child provide the correct answer.) *Yes, choice d is the correct answer. The word <u>gumdrop</u> is made of two words, "gum" and "drop." You should have marked circle <u>d</u>. Does anyone have questions?*

Answer children's questions. Then have children complete questions 8–10.

Comprehension

Have children turn to the Comprehension section of the test (page 9). Then give them these directions.

This part of the test has two reading passages and 10 questions. Read each passage and answer the questions that follow. Mark your answers.

Have children read the passages and answer questions 1–10 independently.

Directions for Scoring the Test

The Grade 2 Placement Test can be scored by section or by total test. On page 174, you will find the Answer Key for this test. It lists the correct response for each question and, in the chart at the bottom, lists the skill measured by each test item. On page 175, you will find a Student Test Results Chart for this test. Make a copy of the chart for each student and use it to record the student's results on each part of the test.

Using the Answer Key, score the tests by marking each item correct or incorrect. Then:
• add up the number of questions answered correctly in each section;
• record the number correct in the space provided on the Student Test Results Chart;
• add the scores to determine the total score.
To find the percentage score for each section and the total test, refer to the Scoring Chart on pages 254–255.

Interpreting Test Results

At the beginning of Grade 2, children who achieve a total test score of 80%–90% should receive on level instruction. Children who score 90% or higher should receive beyond level instruction. Children who score lower than 80% will need approaching level instruction.

Use scores on each section of the test (Phonics, Word Recognition, Vocabulary, and Comprehension) to help make specific instructional plans for each child. For example, a child who scores 80% or higher in three sections but only 60% in Vocabulary would benefit from additional instruction that emphasizes vocabulary development. You may also want to refer to the Tested Skills Chart below the Answer Key to identify the skills measured by those items the child answered incorrectly.

For those children whose scores do not clearly define their areas of weaknesses and strengths, you may need to administer additional assessments. Administer a diagnostic assessment for those students who are significantly below grade level. See page 13 for reference. For children who seem to be significantly above grade level you may want to administer the Placement Test for Grade 3 to collect additional information.

below 80% = A book
80% – 90% = O book
90% or higher = B book

Grade 2 Placement Test
Answer Key

Phonics		Word Recognition	Vocabulary	Comprehension
1. c	11. a	1. c	1. a	1. d
2. a	12. c	2. d	2. c	2. a
3. a	13. a	3. a	3. b	3. d
4. d	14. a	4. c	4. b	4. a
5. d	15. a	5. a	5. a	5. b
6. a	16. a	6. a	6. a	6. c
7. a	17. a	7. a	7. c	7. a
8. a	18. b	8. d	8. a	8. b
9. c	19. a	9. b	9. c	9. b
10. a	20. b	10. b	10. d	10. d

Tested Skills	Item Numbers
Phonics	
Short Vowels	1–4
Long Vowels	5–8
R-Controlled Vowels	9–12
Variant Vowels	13–16
Dipthongs	17–20
Word Recognition	
Recognize High-Frequency Words	1–10
Vocabulary	
Context Clues	1–3
Synonyms and Antonyms	4–7
Compound Words	8–10
Comprehension	
Analyze Character and Plot	1, 2, 3, 5
Make Inferences	4, 8, 9
Main Idea and Supporting Details	6, 7, 10

Placement Test
Grade 3

The Grade 3 Placement Test has three sections and will take about 40 minutes to complete. The chart below shows the sections of the test, the number of test questions, or items, in each section, and the estimated amount of time required for administering each part. You may administer the entire test in several sessions, or you may choose to administer only some parts of the test.

Section	No. of Items	Estimated Time
Word Recognition	10	10 minutes
Vocabulary	10	10 minutes
Comprehension	10	20 minutes
Total	30	40 minutes

Directions for Administering the Test

To begin the administration, have students turn to the Word Recognition section on the first page (page 2) of the test. Read aloud the directions printed in italics below.

Word Recognition

The first part of the test is about recognizing words. For each question, I will read a word aloud. You will look at the four words in the row and find the word I say. Mark your answer by filling in the circle beside the word. Let's do the sample question first.

Sample *Look at the four words in the box marked S. Find the word I say. The word is type. Fill in the circle next to the word type.* (Pause. Then have a student provide the correct answer.) *Yes, choice b is the correct answer. You should have marked circle b. Does anyone have any questions?*

Pause and answer all questions.

Now I will say some more words. Find the word I say in each row. Then mark your answer. Now we will begin. Listen carefully. Read the item number and question. Pause after each question to let students mark their answers.

1. *Find the word <u>another</u>. Mark your answer. The word is <u>another</u>.*
2. *Find the word <u>study</u>.*
3. *Find the word <u>through</u>.*
4. *Find the word <u>glance</u>.*
5. *Find the word <u>important</u>.*
6. *Find the word <u>appear</u>.*
7. *Find the word <u>decide</u>.*

8. Find the word _voice_.
9. Find the word _whisper_.
10. Find the word _country_.

Vocabulary

Have students turn to the vocabulary section on the next page of the test. In this part of the test, read aloud each set of directions and sample questions. Have students answer the questions independently.

Look at part A in the vocabulary section. Follow along as I read the directions:

A. _Read each sentence. Find the meaning of the underlined word. Mark your answer. Let's do the sample question first._

Sample. _Read the sentence in the box marked S. Find the meaning of the underlined word._ (Check to see that students know what to do. Then have a student provide the correct answer.) _Yes, choice a is the correct answer. The word disappear means "vanish." You should have marked circle a. Does anyone have any questions?_

Answer students' questions. Then have students complete questions 1–3. When students are ready, have them turn to the next page and continue with the next part.

Look at part B. Follow along as I read the directions:

B. _Look at the underlined word. Find the word that means the **same** as the underlined word. Mark your answer. Let's do the sample question first._

Sample. _Find the word that means the same as the underlined word._ (Check to see that students know what to do. Then have a student provide the correct answer.) _Yes, choice c is the correct answer. The word shelter means the same as cover. You should have marked circle c. Does anyone have any questions?_

Answer students' questions. Then have students complete questions 4–5. When students are ready, have them continue with the next part.

Look at part C. Follow along as I read the directions:

C. _Look at the underlined word. Find the word that means the **opposite** of the underlined word. Mark your answer. Let's do the sample question first._

Sample. _Find the word that means the opposite of the underlined word._ (Check to see that students know what to do. Then have a student provide a correct answer.) _Yes, choice d is the correct answer. The word prevent means the opposite of cause. You should have marked circle d. Does anyone have any questions?_

Answer students' questions. Then have students complete questions 6–7. When students are ready, have them turn to the next page and continue with the next part.

Look at part D. Follow along as I read the directions:

D. *Read each sentence. Choose the word that correctly completes the sentence. Mark your answer. Let's do the sample question first.*

Sample. *Find the word that correctly completes the sentence.* (Check to see that students know what to do. Then have a student provide the correct answer.) *Yes, choice <u>b</u> is the correct answer. "My sister became ill because she was <u>unhealthy</u>." You should have marked circle <u>b</u>. Does anyone have any questions?*

Answer students' questions. Then have students complete questions 8–10.

Have students turn to the Comprehension section of the test (page 6). Give students the following directions.

This part of the test has two reading passages and 10 questions. Read each passage and answer the questions that follow. Mark your answers.

Have students read the passages and answer questions 1–10 independently.

Directions for Scoring the Test

The Grade 3 Placement Test can be scored by section or by total test. On page 196, you will find the Answer Key for this test. It lists the correct response for each question and, in the chart at the bottom, lists the skill measured by each test item. On page 197, you will find a Student Test Results Chart for this test. Make a copy of the chart for each student and use it to record the student's results on each part of the test.

Using the Answer Key, score the tests by marking each item correct or incorrect. Then:
- add up the number of questions answered correctly in each section;
- record the number correct in the space provided on the Student Results Chart;
- add the scores to determine the total test score.
To find the percentage score for each section and the total test, refer to the Scoring Chart on pages 254–255.

Interpreting Test Results

At the beginning of Grade 3, students who achieve a total test score of 80%–90% should receive on level instruction. Students who score 90% or higher should receive beyond level instruction. Students who score lower than 80% will need approaching level instruction.

Use the scores on each section of the test (Word Recognition, Vocabulary, and Comprehension) to help make specific instructional plans for each student. For example, a student who scores 80% or higher in two sections but only 60% in Vocabulary would benefit from additional instruction that emphasizes vocabulary development. You may also want to refer to the Tested Skills Chart below the

Answer Key to identify the skills measured by those items the student answered incorrectly.

For those students whose scores do not clearly define their weaknesses and strengths, you may need to administer additional assessments. Administer a diagnostic assessment for those students who are significantly below grade level. See page 13 for reference. For students who seem to be significantly above grade level, you may want to administer the Placement Test for Grade 4 to collect additional information.

Grade 3 Placement Test Answer Key

Word Recognition	Vocabulary	Comprehension
1. a	1. c	1. d
2. c	2. c	2. a
3. a	3. b	3. b
4. b	4. d	4. a
5. b	5. d	5. b
6. d	6. b	6. b
7. c	7. b	7. a
8. d	8. d	8. c
9. a	9. b	9. d
10. a	10. d	10. b

Tested Skills	Item Numbers
Word Recognition	
High-Frequency Words	1–10
Vocabulary	
Context Clues	1–3
Synonyms and Antonyms	4–7
Prefixes and Suffixes	8–10
Comprehension	
Analyze Character and Setting	1, 3
Cause and Effect	7, 9
Sequence of Events	2
Compare and Contrast	4
Main Idea and Supporting Details	6, 8
Make Inferences	5, 10

© Macmillan/McGraw-Hill

Placement Assessment · Grade 3

Name _____ Date _____

Grade _____

Student Test Results Chart
Grade 3

Test Section	Number Correct	% Score	Notes
Word Recognition	/10		
Vocabulary	/10		
Comprehension	/10		

Additional Assessments Indicated:

_____

_____

Placement/Instructional Decisions:

_____

_____

Placement Test

Grade 3

Name _____ Date _____

Word Recognition

Find the word your teacher says. Mark your answer.

| S. | Ⓐ trunk | Ⓑ type | Ⓒ trade | Ⓓ trust |

1. Ⓐ another   Ⓑ America   Ⓒ area   Ⓓ among

2. Ⓐ stage   Ⓑ strike   Ⓒ study   Ⓓ stripe

3. Ⓐ through   Ⓑ though   Ⓒ thousand   Ⓓ thoughtful

4. Ⓐ giggle   Ⓑ glance   Ⓒ geese   Ⓓ gleam

5. Ⓐ invent   Ⓑ important   Ⓒ information   Ⓓ impossible

6. Ⓐ peer   Ⓑ appeal   Ⓒ perform   Ⓓ appear

7. Ⓐ deserted   Ⓑ discover   Ⓒ decide   Ⓓ design

8. Ⓐ vegetable   Ⓑ voyage   Ⓒ vast   Ⓓ voice

9. Ⓐ whisper   Ⓑ wonderful   Ⓒ wisdom   Ⓓ wrinkle

10. Ⓐ country   Ⓑ complete   Ⓒ culture   Ⓓ celebrate

Vocabulary

A. Read each sentence. Find the meaning of the underlined word. Mark your answer.

S. The clouds made the mountain tops disappear.
The word disappear means

Ⓐ vanish.　　　　　Ⓒ rise.

Ⓑ return.　　　　　Ⓓ fall.

---

1. The family enjoyed the wonderful day they spent at the water fun park. The word enjoyed means

   Ⓐ followed.　　　　Ⓒ loved.

   Ⓑ watched.　　　　Ⓓ found.

2. We gathered as much wood as we could find to make a camp fire. The word gathered means

   Ⓐ lost.　　　　　Ⓒ collected.

   Ⓑ sold.　　　　　Ⓓ practiced.

3. Lara combined the milk and eggs in a bowl, and then she poured in some flour. The word combined means

   Ⓐ created.　　　　Ⓒ cleaned.

   Ⓑ mixed together.　　Ⓓ broke apart.

Name _____ Date _____

Vocabulary

B. Look at the underlined word. Find the word that means the **same** as the underlined word. Mark your answer.

S. gives <u>shelter</u>
Ⓐ water Ⓑ food Ⓒ cover Ⓓ family

4. a <u>creepy</u> movie
Ⓐ funny Ⓑ pleasant Ⓒ tasty Ⓓ scary

5. <u>blooming</u> flowers
Ⓐ dying Ⓑ hanging Ⓒ moving Ⓓ growing

C. Look at the underlined word. Find the word that means the **opposite** of the underlined word. Mark your answer.

S. to <u>prevent</u> sunburn
Ⓐ change Ⓑ heal Ⓒ ask Ⓓ cause

6. to <u>fetch</u> a ball
Ⓐ bring back Ⓑ carry away Ⓒ throw Ⓓ toss

7. to <u>remember</u>
Ⓐ whisper Ⓑ forget Ⓒ listen Ⓓ create

Vocabulary

D. Read each sentence. Choose the word that correctly completes the sentence. Mark your answer.

S. My sister became ill because she was _____.

  Ⓐ healthful   Ⓒ healthy

  Ⓑ unhealthy   Ⓓ health

---

8. The students were _____ that their teacher would not assign homework during spring vacation week.

  Ⓐ hopeless   Ⓒ hopes

  Ⓑ hope   Ⓓ hopeful

9. The students are much _____ since they started listening to soft music in the classroom.

  Ⓐ calmly   Ⓒ calmness

  Ⓑ calmer   Ⓓ calming

10. The bright, beautiful birds in the rain forest are so _____!

  Ⓐ colorless   Ⓒ colors

  Ⓑ coloring   Ⓓ colorful

Comprehension

Read each passage and answer the questions that follow.

Friends

One day, a young bear, a beaver, and a racoon were playing hide-and-seek in the woods. A small brown rabbit came hopping down the path and asked to play.

"Sure," said the bear, "you can join us."

"Let's play catch," said Rabbit.

"Oh, but we're playing hide-and-seek," said Beaver. Bear looked at Beaver. "All right, we'll play catch," Beaver agreed.

The animals had not played catch for very long before Rabbit demanded, "Let's play leapfrog!"

"We're playing catch," said Racoon.

"I'm tired of playing catch," moaned Rabbit.

"Okay," said Bear, who was a bit upset but wanted to be nice to their new friend. The animals switched to leapfrog, but not for long. Rabbit soon complained, "I'm sick of this game. Let's play tag!"

Beaver had had enough. He said, "I have to go home now." Then he turned and walked away.

"I think I hear my mom calling. See you later!" said Bear, who headed toward the hills.

"I have to go, too," said Racoon.

Rabbit was left all alone.

Third Grade Comprehension Questions – Friends

1. Where does this story take place?
   Ⓐ at school
   Ⓒ by a pond
   Ⓑ on a playground
   Ⓓ in the woods

2. What were the animals playing first?
   Ⓐ hide-and-seek
   Ⓒ leapfrog
   Ⓑ catch
   Ⓓ tag

3. Which word best describes Rabbit?
   Ⓐ funny
   Ⓒ caring
   Ⓑ selfish
   Ⓓ worried

4. Compare how did the animals felt before Rabbit came and at the end of the story.
   Ⓐ First they were happy, then they were upset.
   Ⓑ First they were sad, then they were happy.
   Ⓒ First they were bored, then they were afraid.
   Ⓓ First they were angry, then they were sad.

5. Why did Bear say, "I think I hear my mom calling. See you later!" when Rabbit said he wanted to play tag?
   Ⓐ Bear really did hear his mom calling him for dinner.
   Ⓑ Bear was tired of switching games for Rabbit and lost interest in playing.
   Ⓒ Bear was going to secretly play a game with Rabbit after Beaver went home.
   Ⓓ Bear was going to going to Beaver's house.

Protecting the Gorillas

Forty years ago, there were not many gorillas left in Africa. Wild gorillas were being killed by hunters, and they would soon all be gone. A woman named Dian Fossey helped change that.

Dr. Fossey was from California. She was born in 1932. She loved working with animals, so she went to Africa in 1963. There she met a scientist named Dr. Louis Leakey. Dr. Leakey was studying great apes. Dian Fossey began learning about apes, too. She studied mountain gorillas.

Dr. Fossey spent some time studying gorillas in Zaire and in Rwanda. She wanted to prove that gorillas could be gentle animals, and could become friends with people. In 1967, she built a camp in the mountains called Karisoke. She lived there for a long time.

In 1970, a gorilla named Peanuts reached out and touched Dr. Fossey's hand. It was the first time a gorilla had ever touched a person in a friendly way. Before long, the wild gorillas all came to trust Dr. Fossey. This helped her understand more about the way gorillas behave. She was the first person to be this close with gorillas.

Dr. Fossey spent the rest of her life working to protect mountain gorillas. Her favorite gorilla, Digit, was killed by hunters. Dr. Fossey told the world about Digit in a story she wrote for *National Geographic* magazine. Many people read Dr. Fosseys's story and wanted to send money to help protect the gorillas.

A few years later, Dr. Fossey wrote a book called *Gorillas in the Mist*, and it was made into a movie. This story of her work helped people around the world understand more about gorillas. By the early 1980's, there were about 250 wild gorillas in Africa. Dr. Fossey died in 1985, but her work lives on. Today, there are many more wild mountain gorillas. Scientists still work at Karisoke to protect the gorillas, and—thanks to Dr. Fossey— we know more about the great apes than ever before.

6. What is the main idea of this passage?
   - Ⓐ A gorilla named Peanuts touched Dr. Fossey's hand.
   - Ⓑ Dian Fossey spent much of her life studying and protecting gorillas.
   - Ⓒ Most of the gorillas in Africa were killed by hunters.
   - Ⓓ Dian Fossey was born in California in 1932 and went to Africa in 1963.

7. Dian Fossey went to Africa because she wanted to
   - Ⓐ work with animals.
   - Ⓑ meet with Dr. Leakey.
   - Ⓒ build a camp.
   - Ⓓ write a magazine story.

8. Which detail shows that gorillas could be gentle and friendly to people?

    Ⓐ Dr. Fossey built a camp near the gorillas.

    Ⓑ She wrote an article about a gorilla.

    Ⓒ Peanuts touched Dr. Fossey's hand.

    Ⓓ Scientists still work at Karisoke today.

9. Why did people give money to Dr. Fossey to help the gorillas?

    Ⓐ Dr. Leakey asked people to send money.

    Ⓑ They wanted her to make a movie about gorillas.

    Ⓒ She had built a camp in the mountains.

    Ⓓ They read about her work in a magazine.

10. Why did Dr. Fossey want to live in the mountains?

    Ⓐ She loved the outdoors.

    Ⓑ She wanted to live near the gorillas.

    Ⓒ She was bored living in the city.

    Ⓓ She wanted to learn how to hunt.

Placement Test
Grade 4

The Grade 4 Placement Test has two sections and will take about 40 minutes to complete. The chart below shows the sections of the test, the number of test questions, or items, in each section, and the estimated amount of time required for administering each part. You may administer the entire test in several sessions, or you may choose to administer only some parts of the test.

Section	No. of Items	Estimated Time
Vocabulary	15	15 minutes
Comprehension	16	25 minutes
Total	31	40 minutes

Directions for Administering the Test

To begin the administration, have students look at the front cover of the test and follow along as you read the directions aloud:

This is a test of reading and vocabulary. For each part of the test, read the directions carefully. Then answer the questions. Mark your answer to each question by filling in the circle beside the answer you choose.

Have students read the sample question by themselves and fill in the circle beside the answer. Give students time to complete the question. Then have a student provide the correct answer. Discuss the sample question with students and make sure they know how to answer the questions. Then have them turn to the appropriate page and begin the test. Tell students which part(s) of the test they should complete and how much time they will have to finish each part.

For Vocabulary, students should read the directions for each part and answer questions 1–15 independently. For Comprehension, have students read the passages and answer questions 1–16 independently.

Directions for Scoring the Test

The Grade 4 Placement Test can be scored by section or by total test. On page 212, you will find the Answer Key for this test. It lists the correct response for each question and, in the chart at the bottom, lists the skill measured by each test item. On page 213, you will find a Student Test Results Chart for this test. Make a copy of the chart for each student and use it to record the student's results on each part of the test.

Using the Answer Key, score the tests by marking each item correct or incorrect. Then:
- add up the number of questions answered correctly in each section;
- record the number correct in the space provided on the Student Test Results Chart;
- add the scores to determine the test scores.

To find the percentage score for each section and the total test, refer to the scoring Chart on pages 254–255.

Interpreting Test Results

At the beginning of Grade 4, students who achieve a total test score of 80%–90% should receive on level reading instruction. Students who score 90% or higher should receive beyond level instruction. Students who score lower than 80% should receive approaching level instruction.

Use the scores on each section of the test (Vocabulary and Comprehension) to help make specific instructional plans for each student. For example, a student who scores 80% or higher in Comprehension but only 60% in Vocabulary would benefit from additional instruction that emphasizes vocabulary development. You may also want to refer to the Tested Skills Chart below the Answer Key to identify the skills measured by those items the student answered incorrectly.

For those students whose scores do not clearly define their weaknesses and strengths, you may need to administer additional assessments. Administer a diagnostic assessment for those students who are significantly below grade level. See page 13 for reference. For students who seem to be significantly above grade level, you may want to administer the Placement Test for Grade 5 to collect additional information.

Grade 4 Placement Test
Answer Key

Vocabulary
1. c
2. b
3. d
4. c
5. a
6. b
7. b
8. a
9. b
10. a
11. a
12. b
13. d
14. c
15. a

Comprehension
1. c
2. a
3. d
4. c
5. a
6. b
7. c
8. b
9. c
10. d
11. b
12. c
13. a
14. d
15. c
16. d

Tested Skills	Item Numbers
Vocabulary	
Context Clues	1–3
Multiple-Meaning Words	4–6
Synonyms and Antonyms	7–9
Prefixes and Suffixes	10–12
Root Words	13–15
Comprehension	
Analyze Character and Setting	1, 2
Make Inferences	5, 7
Main Idea and Supporting Details	8, 9
Sequence of Events	3, 10, 16
Cause and Effect	4, 11
Evaluate Author's Purpose, Point of View	12
Compare and Contrast	6, 13
Distinguish Between Fact and Opinion	14, 15

Name _____ Date _____

Grade _____

Student Test Results Chart

Grade 4

Test Section	Number Correct	% Score	Notes
Vocabulary	/15		
Comprehension	/16		
Total	/31		

Additional Assessments Indicated:

_____

_____

Placement/Instructional Decisions:

_____

_____

Student's Name _____ Date _____

Teacher's Name _____ Grade _____

Placement Test
Grade 4

This is a test of reading and vocabulary. For each part of the test, read the directions carefully. Then answer the questions. Mark your answer to each question by filling in the circle beside the answer you choose.

Sample

Read the sentence. Find the meaning of the underlined word. Mark your answer.

Ms. Branley lives in that yellow house in the <u>village</u>.
The word <u>village</u> means

Ⓐ apartment building.

Ⓑ small town.

Ⓒ parking lot.

Ⓓ large church.

Vocabulary

A. Read each sentence. Find the meaning of the underlined word or words. Mark your answer.

1. All of the kids <u>chuckled</u> when Mr. Rodriguez came into the classroom dressed up like the school mascot on School Spirit Day. The word <u>chuckled</u> means
   - Ⓐ carried.
   - Ⓑ discovered.
   - Ⓒ laughed.
   - Ⓓ heard.

2. We took many <u>photographs</u> to remember our family vacation in Florida. The word <u>photographs</u> means
   - Ⓐ boxes.
   - Ⓑ pictures.
   - Ⓒ memories.
   - Ⓓ suitcases.

3. Everyone who has read Leo's book has loved it; they all feel like it will be his <u>masterpiece</u>. In this sentence, <u>masterpiece</u> means
   - Ⓐ choice.
   - Ⓑ biggest.
   - Ⓒ first chance.
   - Ⓓ greatest work.

4. On Saturday, the first chore that Juan <u>scratched</u> off his list of chores was getting gas for the car. In this sentence, the word <u>scratched</u> means
   - Ⓐ scraped.
   - Ⓑ cut.
   - Ⓒ crossed.
   - Ⓓ finished.

5. Josie wears a purple dress because the deep color really <u>suits</u> her. In this sentence, the word <u>suits</u> means
   - Ⓐ flatters.
   - Ⓑ coats.
   - Ⓒ clothing.
   - Ⓓ costumes.

6. Cows <u>produce</u> milk naturally. In this sentence, the word <u>produce</u> means
   - Ⓐ fruit and vegetables.
   - Ⓑ make.
   - Ⓒ discover.
   - Ⓓ buy.

Name _____ Date _____

7. Every morning, the principal <u>announces</u> over the loudspeaker what will be served for lunch that day. The word <u>announces</u> means
   (A) listens.   (B) reports.   (C) hides.   (D) ignores.

8. Min bought a <u>sturdy</u> table from the furniture store because she needed to put a heavy television on it. Which word means the same as <u>sturdy</u>?
   (A) strong   (B) weak   (C) soft   (D) wide

9. To stay <u>healthy</u>, a person should eat a balanced diet of meats, vegetables, and fruits. Which word means the **opposite** of <u>healthy</u>?
   (A) fit   (B) ill   (C) well   (D) perfect

10. The <u>untrusting</u> children did not talk to the strangers. <u>Untrusting</u> means
    (A) not trusting.   (C) very trusting.
    (B) always trusting.   (D) trusting too much.

11. The workers spent long hours trying to <u>rebuild</u> the fence. The word <u>rebuild</u> means
    (A) build again.   (B) build well.   (C) build before.   (D) build poorly.

12. It is important to wear sun protection because the sun's rays are <u>harmful</u>. The word <u>harmful</u> means
    (A) without harm.   (C) against harm.
    (B) full of harm.   (D) not enough harm.

13. Which word most likely comes from the root word *tele*, meaning "far off"?
    (A) retell   (C) towel
    (B) storyteller   (D) telescope

14. Which word most likely comes from the root word *just*, meaning "law"?
    (A) juice   (C) justice
    (B) juggle   (D) jump

15. Which word most likely comes from the word *astro*, meaning "star"?
    (A) asteroid   (C) artist
    (B) asleep   (D) aside

Comprehension

Read each passage and answer the questions that follow.

The Animal Hunt

Yesterday was my brother Ben's fifth birthday party. As usual, since I'm the older sister, I had to help out. Mom said, "Leslie, five busy boys need to be watched carefully. You can't let them out of your sight for a minute or you'll lose one." Then she put me in charge of the games.

Since I didn't want to lose anybody, I planned only one game for the boys to play outside. Ben loved animals and looking for hidden things. So I took ten of his plastic toy animals and hid them in the vacant lot next to our apartment building. By the time I was done, there were three bears, two snakes, three monkeys, one giraffe, and one lion hidden all over the lot.

When Ben's four friends arrived for the party, I could hardly believe how noisy and excited they were. Mom said, "Leslie, I'm going to cook the pizza. You can play your game outside with the boys. Then bring them in to eat."

"Okay, Ben," I announced. "It's time to go on a safari. The boy who finds the most animals will win a prize. I have hidden ten toy animals in the empty lot. Meet me out front in one minute." The boys raced down the stairs. Then they lined up on the sidewalk ready to begin.

"On your mark, get set, go!" I cried, pointing them all toward the lot next door.

Ben and his friends tore around the lot looking under the rocks and in the grass. They shrieked and laughed as they discovered eight of the animals. Only the giraffe and a snake were still hidden. Then I noticed Chris, Ben's best friend. He was waving a snake around calling, "I found the snake!"

As I looked more closely, I knew it was not one of the thick, black, rubber snakes that I had hidden. This snake was long and thin. "Drop it, drop it!" I screamed. I had no idea whether this kind of snake was dangerous or not, but I was not going to take any chances.

Chris threw the snake up into the air. I ran over just in time to see its tail disappear under a rock. Suddenly my heart was pumping wildly. "Chris, that snake was alive! I never hid that snake. Did it bite you?" I questioned him and carefully examined his hands and arms.

He replied calmly. "No, I just picked it up and then threw it when you told me to." He looked at me and asked, "Will it count toward the prize?"

"Yes, of course," I answered, chuckling in spite of myself. Then I warned the boys, "Be careful not to pick up anything that is alive. The toy snakes are black and thick."

The rest of the game passed in slow motion for me. The boys dashed around and poked in the dirt. As soon as they uncovered the last two animals, I hurried them upstairs before anything else could happen.

Everyone agreed that Chris was the winner. He found three toy animals and one living snake!

1. Where do Ben and his sister live?
    Ⓐ on a farm
    Ⓑ in the woods
    Ⓒ in an apartment building
    Ⓓ beside a zoo

2. Which word best describes Ben's sister Leslie?
    Ⓐ helpful
    Ⓑ silly
    Ⓒ selfish
    Ⓓ brave

3. What happened just after Chris threw the snake into the air?
    Ⓐ Leslie made the boys go inside.
    Ⓑ Ben's mom made a pizza.
    Ⓒ The boys lined up on the sidewalk.
    Ⓓ The snake went under a rock.

4. Leslie was probably upset by the snake because she
   Ⓐ did not want one of the boys to get lost.
   Ⓑ forgot where she put it.
   Ⓒ was worried that the snake would bite Chris.
   Ⓓ did not like toy snakes.

5. Why did the rest of the game go in slow motion for Leslie?
   Ⓐ Leslie was still in shock that Chris picked up a snake.
   Ⓑ Leslie was in a trance.
   Ⓒ Leslie couldn't wait for the party to begin.
   Ⓓ Leslie was bored.

6. How was Leslie different after Chris picked up the snake?
   Ⓐ She did not want to help with the party anymore.
   Ⓑ She was worried about the boys.
   Ⓒ She felt more confident about herself.
   Ⓓ She thought that time went by too fast.

7. By the end of the day, what did Leslie most likely learn?
   Ⓐ Children like to eat pizza.
   Ⓑ Birthday parties are fun.
   Ⓒ Children do need to be watched carefully.
   Ⓓ Most birthday parties are peaceful and quiet.

Dr. Drew: A Great American

Every year, about 8 million Americans give blood to help others. This blood is saved in places called "blood banks." Then it is used to help people who are injured or become sick. How can blood be saved in a bank until it is needed? The work of an African-American man named Charles Drew made it possible.

Charles Richard Drew was born in Washington, D.C., in 1904. In school, Charles got good grades, and he was always good in sports. In high school, he was named best all-around athlete. He did especially well in track and football. He probably could have become a professional athlete, but he decided not to. When Charles was 15 years old, his sister died of tuberculosis. That is a disease of the lungs. After experiencing his sister's illness, Charles decided to become a doctor. He first attended college in Baltimore and then went to McGill University in Montreal, Canada, to become a doctor. There he met Dr. John Beattie, who was one of his teachers. Charles Drew became interested in Dr. Beattie's work with blood. He soon began reading all he could about blood. He and Dr. Beattie became good friends. They worked together until Charles finished school.

Dr. Drew continued to study blood. In 1938, he wrote an important paper called "Banked Blood." It was about the best ways to save blood in a blood bank. Drew discovered new ways to store large amounts of blood— and just in time! Drew made his discovery just when the fighting of World War II began. A lot of blood was needed to save wounded soldiers, and Dr. Drew was the man to collect it. In 1941, he became the head of the American Red Cross Blood Bank in New York. He was in charge of the blood that would be used for the U.S. Army and Navy.

Dr. Charles Drew and his work probably saved millions of lives during the war and in the years since then. He was a remarkable man. To honor Dr. Drew, the U.S. Postal Service issued a stamp with his picture on it in 1981. The stamp was part of a special series called "Great Americans."

8. What is this passage mostly about?
   Ⓐ a series of stamps called "Great Americans"
   Ⓑ Dr. Charles Drew and his work with blood
   Ⓒ why Dr. Drew went to school in Canada
   Ⓓ how the United States got into World War II

9. Which detail supports the idea that Charles Drew was a "Great American"?
   Ⓐ He grew up in Washington, D.C.
   Ⓑ He went to McGill University in Canada.
   Ⓒ His discovery saved millions of lives.
   Ⓓ He wrote a paper called "Banked Blood."

10. What did Charles Drew do just after high school?
    Ⓐ He became a professional athlete.
    Ⓑ He wrote a paper about blood.
    Ⓒ He joined the U.S. Army.
    Ⓓ He went to college.

11. Charles Drew decided to become a doctor because
    Ⓐ he was not very good at sports.
    Ⓑ he lost his sister to a disease.
    Ⓒ he always got good grades in school.
    Ⓓ he knew that people needed him.

12. The purpose of this passage is to
    Ⓐ persuade people to give blood.
    Ⓑ compare Charles Drew with other doctors.
    Ⓒ give information about Charles Drew.
    Ⓓ tell an entertaining story about Charles Drew.

13. Before Dr. Charles Drew made his discovery, people did not know how to
    Ⓐ store large amounts of blood.
    Ⓑ become professional athletes.
    Ⓒ recognize different kinds of disease.
    Ⓓ save soldiers who were wounded.

14. Which sentence states a fact?
    Ⓐ Charles was always a good student.
    Ⓑ Charles was always good in sports.
    Ⓒ Charles excelled in track and football.
    Ⓓ Charles's sister died of tuberculosis.

15. Which sentence states an opinion?
    Ⓐ Charles decided to become a doctor.
    Ⓑ Charles went to college in Baltimore, Maryland.
    Ⓒ Dr. Drew was a remarkable man.
    Ⓓ The U.S. Postal Service issued a stamp to honor Charles.

16. What did Dr. Drew do just after World War II began?
    Ⓐ He became a doctor.
    Ⓑ He went to McGill University.
    Ⓒ He wrote a paper called "Banked Blood."
    Ⓓ He became the head of the American Red Cross Blood Bank.

Placement Test

Grade 5

The Grade 5 Placement Test has two sections and will take about 45 minutes to complete. The chart below shows the sections of the test, the number of test questions, or items, in each section, and the estimated amount of time required for administering each part. You may administer the entire test in several sessions, or you may choose to administer only some parts of the test.

Section	No. of Items	Estimated Time
Vocabulary	20	20 minutes
Comprehension	16	25 minutes
Total	36	45 minutes

Directions for Administering the Test

To begin the administration, have students look at the front cover of the test and follow along as you read the directions aloud:

This is a test of reading and vocabulary. For each part of the test, read the directions carefully. Then answer the questions. Mark your answer to each question by filling in the circle beside the answer you choose.

Have students read the sample question by themselves and fill in the circle beside the answer. Give students time to complete the question. Then have a student provide the correct answer. Discuss the sample question with students and make sure they know how to answer the questions. Then have them turn to the appropriate page and begin the test. Tell students which part(s) of the test they should complete and how much time they will have to finish each part.

For Vocabulary, students should read the directions for each part and answer questions 1–20 independently. For Comprehension, have students read the passages and answer questions 1–16 independently.

Directions for Scoring the Test

The Grade 5 Placement Test can be scored by section or by total test. On page 226, you will find the Answer Key for this test. It lists the correct response for each question and, in the chart at the bottom, lists the skill measured by each test item. On page 227, you will find a Student Test Results Chart for this test. Make a copy of the chart for each student and use it to record the student's results on each part of the test.

Using the Answer Key, score the tests by marking each item correct or incorrect. Then:
- add up the number of questions answered correctly in each section;
- record the number correct in the space provided on the Student Test Results Chart;
- add the scores to determine the test scores.

To find the percentage score for each section and the total test, refer to the Scoring Chart on pages 254–255.

Interpreting Test Results

At the beginning of Grade 5, students who achieve a total test score of 80%–90% should receive on level instruction. Students who score 90% or higher should receive beyond level instruction. Students who score lower than 80% should receive approaching level instruction.

Use the scores on each section of the test (Vocabulary and Comprehension) to help make specific instructional plans for each student. For example, a student who scores 80% or higher in Comprehension but only 60% in Vocabulary would benefit from additional instruction that emphasizes vocabulary development. You may also want to refer to the Tested Skills Chart below the Answer Key to identify the skills measured by those items the student answered incorrectly.

If you have students whose scores do not clearly define their weaknesses and strengths, you may need to administer additional assessments. Administer a diagnostic assessment for those students who are significantly below grade level. See page 13 for reference. For students who seem to be significantly above grade level, you may want to administer the Placement Test for Grade 6 to collect additional information.

Grade 5 Placement Test
Answer Key

Vocabulary

1. b	11. c
2. b	12. d
3. a	13. b
4. d	14. b
5. a	15. c
6. b	16. a
7. d	17. a
8. c	18. b
9. b	19. d
10. c	20. b

Comprehension

1. b	11. c
2. c	12. d
3. a	13. d
4. c	14. a
5. b	15. a
6. d	16. b
7. c	
8. a	
9. d	
10. b	

Tested Skills	Item Numbers
Vocabulary	
Context Clues	1–5
Multiple-Meaning Words	6–8
Synonyms and Antonyms	9–12
Prefixes and Suffixes	13–16
Root Words	17–20
Comprehension	
Analyze Character and Setting	1, 4
Make Inferences	7, 12
Main Idea and Supporting Details	8, 9
Sequence of Events	2, 3
Cause and Effect	5, 11
Evaluate Author's Purpose, Point of View	10, 13
Compare and Contrast	6, 15
Distinguish Between Fact and Opinion	14, 16

Name _____ Date _____

Grade _____

Student Test Results Chart
Grade 5

Test Section	Number Correct	% Score	Notes
Vocabulary	/20		
Comprehension	/16		
Total	/36		

Additional Assessments Indicated:

_____

_____

Placement/Instructional Decisions:

_____

_____

Student's Name _____ Date _____

Teacher's Name _____ Grade _____

Placement Test
Grade 5

This a test of reading and vocabulary. For each part of the test, read the directions carefully. Then answer the questions. Mark your answer to each question by filling in the circle beside the answer you choose.

Sample

Read the sentence. Find the meaning of the underlined word. Mark your answer.

Theo went into the kitchen to <u>prepare</u> lunch for everyone. The word <u>prepare</u> means

Ⓐ eat quickly.

Ⓑ try to sell.

Ⓒ make ready.

Ⓓ get rid of.

Vocabulary

A. Read each sentence. Find the meaning of the underlined word or words. Mark your answer.

1. The wind <u>scattered</u> the fall leaves around the yard. The word <u>scattered</u> means
   - Ⓐ combined.
   - Ⓑ spread out.
   - Ⓒ sorted.
   - Ⓓ mixed in.

2. Dad decided to buy a car that <u>consumes</u> less gas than his old car. The word <u>consumes</u> means
   - Ⓐ collects.
   - Ⓑ uses.
   - Ⓒ buys.
   - Ⓓ produces.

3. Snakes are often seen <u>coiled</u> around tree branches. The word <u>coiled</u> means
   - Ⓐ curled.
   - Ⓑ backwards.
   - Ⓒ flat.
   - Ⓓ straight.

4. When I fight with my sister, Mom says, "Stop making a <u>ruckus</u>." The word <u>ruckus</u> means
   - Ⓐ a mess.
   - Ⓑ a mistake.
   - Ⓒ a lot of work.
   - Ⓓ a lot of noise

5. The puddle <u>evaporated</u> when the sun came out. The word <u>evaporated</u> means
   - Ⓐ dried up.
   - Ⓑ froze.
   - Ⓒ got larger.
   - Ⓓ bubbled.

6. We all felt <u>faint</u> in summer school when the air conditioners stopped working. In this sentence, <u>faint</u> means

   Ⓐ good.

   Ⓑ weak.

   Ⓒ small.

   Ⓓ smart.

7. During gym <u>period</u>, Domingo twisted his ankle playing soccer. In this sentence, the word <u>period</u> means

   Ⓐ exercise.

   Ⓑ school.

   Ⓒ a punctuation mark.

   Ⓓ an amount of time.

8. We were careful to steer our canoe away from the river's swift <u>current</u>. In this sentence, the word <u>current</u> means

   Ⓐ in the present time.

   Ⓑ shore.

   Ⓒ movement of water.

   Ⓓ ice.

B. Choose the best answer to each question. Mark your answer.

9. Bird-watching can be a <u>solitary</u> hobby. Which word means the **same** as <u>solitary</u>?

   Ⓐ expensive

   Ⓑ lonely

   Ⓒ crowded

   Ⓓ painful

10. Mary was <u>anxious</u> to start her new job. Which word means the **same** as <u>anxious</u>?

   Ⓐ excited   Ⓒ nervous

   Ⓑ happy   Ⓓ calm

11. We prepared too much food for the party and had to <u>discard</u> most of it. Which word means the **opposite** of <u>discard</u>?

  Ⓐ hold

  Ⓑ make

  Ⓒ keep

  Ⓓ wrap

12. The <u>brittle</u> twig was easy to break. Which word means the **opposite** of <u>brittle</u>?

  Ⓐ thorny   Ⓒ small

  Ⓑ sharp   Ⓓ strong

13. The <u>glorious</u> sunset had colors that included bright reds, yellows, oranges, and purples. The word <u>glorious</u> means

  Ⓐ opposite of glory.

  Ⓑ filled with glory.

  Ⓒ against glory.

  Ⓓ having no glory.

14. She walked into her surprise party, completely <u>unsuspecting</u>. The word <u>unsuspecting</u> means

  Ⓐ suspectful.

  Ⓑ not suspecting.

  Ⓒ suspectful before.

  Ⓓ full of suspect.

15. We knew that the barking dog behind our neighbor's front door was actually <u>harmless</u>. The word <u>harmless</u> means

  Ⓐ having much harm.

  Ⓑ against harm.

  Ⓒ without harm.

  Ⓓ after the harm.

16. The <u>indignity</u> of his act offended me. The word <u>indignity</u> means

  Ⓐ without dignity.   Ⓒ against dignity.

  Ⓑ full of dignity.   Ⓓ with some dignity.

17. Which word most likely comes from the root word *numer*, meaning "quantity"?

   Ⓐ numerous

   Ⓑ numb

   Ⓒ merry

   Ⓓ enough

18. Which word most likely comes from the root word *magn*, meaning "great"?

   Ⓐ maid

   Ⓑ magnify

   Ⓒ magpie

   Ⓓ magic

19. Which word most likely comes from the root word *paleo*, meaning "old"?

   Ⓐ pale

   Ⓑ pageant

   Ⓒ painter

   Ⓓ paleontologist

20. Which word most likely comes from the root word *terr*, meaning "earth"?

   Ⓐ terrify

   Ⓑ territory

   Ⓒ terrible

   Ⓓ terrific

Comprehension

Read each passage and answer the questions that follow.

The Lesson

Last fall, a new kid moved to town. His name was Prescott Howard. As if his name weren't formal enough, he also wore a shirt and tie to school every day. When he spoke, he used the kind of language you would use if you were writing a paper for school. He never participated when we played at recess or after school, even though we always invited him to play. He just hung around and watched with his hands in his pockets.

One day after school, Billy, Marta, Jamal, and I were playing ball at the park. Toby, my dog, was tearing back and forth, barking frantically and trying to catch the ball. Pretty soon there was Prescott, sitting on a bench and watching. We ignored him and kept playing. None of us noticed that Toby had disappeared.

Jamal had just scooped up a tough ground ball when we heard brakes squeal. There was a sharp yelp and then the sound of someone driving away fast. I ran toward the street, but when I got there, Prescott was already kneeling by Toby, talking softly to him. Then I saw the most horrible thing. A bone was sticking out of Toby's back leg. I knelt by his head and put out my hand.

"Don't, Betsy," Prescott said sharply. "He won't recognize you right now, and he might bite you. Give me your jacket." Prescott put his hands underneath Toby and slid him onto the jacket. He was so gentle that Toby barely flinched. Prescott flagged down Ms. Ortega, who happened to be driving by, and asked me, "Who's your vet?"

"Dr. Swanson, on Third Street," I said. Prescott opened the car door and asked Ms. Ortega to take us to Third Street.

Toby didn't look good at all. His tongue was hanging out of his mouth and his eyes were glazed. "Will he be okay?" I blurted out.

"Should be," Prescott said calmly, "if your vet is any good." We pulled up in front of Dr. Swanson's office, and Prescott thanked Ms. Ortega. Dr. Swanson rushed Toby into surgery while Prescott and I sat in the waiting room.

"How'd you learn to take care of animals like that?" I asked.

"My mom's a vet," he said. "I used to help her out."

"Well, where's your mom now?"

"She's sick. She had to go to a clinic far away and my dad went with her, so I came to live with my grandmother for a while. Dad grew up in this town."

I didn't know what to say. I felt awkward and awful. Finally I said stupidly, "I guess you ruined your clothes." There was oil from the road on his pants and a bloodstain on his white shirt.

"I know, isn't it great?" Prescott said happily. I stared at him like he was crazy, and finally he sighed and said, "Grams is nice, but she's old-fashioned. She thinks I should wear a shirt and tie to school. Every afternoon we have tea, and dinner is formal, too. She says I don't speak 'correctly.'" He paused, then added, "Dad asked me to do whatever she asked, and I don't want to let him down."

Boy, had I been wrong about this kid! Just then Dr. Swanson came out. "Betsy, Toby will be fine when his leg heals," he said. "Thank your friend here for knowing what to do and getting Toby here before he really went into shock."

I looked at Prescott, who was smiling widely. On the way out I said, "Maybe we could try to explain to your grandmother about clothes, and, uh . . . your name's okay and all, but it's kind of formal."

"My mom calls me Scotty," he said shyly.

"Then come on, Scotty," I said, "we've got to go tell everyone Toby's going to be all right." I clapped him on the shoulder. "And, hey, Scotty, why don't you lose the tie, just for today?"

He pulled off his tie and stuffed it in his pocket. "Race you to your house," he said, and took off. He was actually pretty fast, but he had on dress shoes, so I beat him.

1. Where were the kids at the beginning of this story?
   Ⓐ in school   Ⓒ on the playground
   Ⓑ at the park   Ⓓ at the vet's office

2. According to Betsy, what was Prescott's problem at the beginning?
   Ⓐ He did not like dogs.   Ⓒ He never played with the other kids.
   Ⓑ He could not run very fast.   Ⓓ He was living with his grandmother.

3. What happened just after Prescott came to watch Betsy and her friends play ball?
    Ⓐ Betsy's dog got hit by a car.
    Ⓑ Prescott flagged down Ms. Ortega.
    Ⓒ Betsy and Scotty raced each other to Betsy's house.
    Ⓓ Prescott took off his tie.

4. Which word best describes Prescott's manner with animals?
    Ⓐ silly
    Ⓑ timid
    Ⓒ gentle
    Ⓓ rough

5. Prescott flagged down Ms. Ortega because he
    Ⓐ thought Ms. Ortega had hit Toby.
    Ⓑ needed to take Toby to a vet.
    Ⓒ wanted Ms. Ortega to call the police.
    Ⓓ needed a ride home.

6. How was Prescott different from the other kids at first?
    Ⓐ He was a better ball player.
    Ⓑ He was much older.
    Ⓒ He was a better student.
    Ⓓ He was more formal.

7. From this experience, Betsy probably learned that
    Ⓐ everybody likes to play baseball.
    Ⓑ dogs should not be allowed in the park.
    Ⓒ she should not judge people so quickly.
    Ⓓ you can't count on anyone but yourself.

From Ostrich to Kiwi

Cassowary, emu, ostrich, kiwi. What are these strange words? They are all names of birds that cannot fly. While these flightless birds are alike in some ways, there are important differences among these odd creatures.

The ostrich is the largest living bird. It may weigh over 300 pounds and stand up to ten feet tall. Its very long neck, small head, and long, thin legs give it an awkward appearance. The ostrich has beautiful, soft plumage, or feathers. It grazes on the African plains. The ostrich can run up to 35 miles an hour. It can also defend itself with its two large, clawed toes.

The Australian emu looks much like an ostrich but is smaller. It weighs about 120 pounds and stands six feet tall. It can run up to 30 miles an hour and is a good swimmer. The plumage of the emu is hairlike, not feathery. Emus defend themselves by kicking.

The Australian cassowary has a bony crest on its head. Like a rooster, it has red folds of skin that hang down through the neck. Cassowaries have rough and thick hair. They can grow up to six feet tall. They are bold fighters with long, sharp claws on their toes. They have even been known to kill people with their strong kicks.

The odd-looking New Zealand kiwi stands only a foot high. It weighs between 3 and 9 pounds. Its wings are so tiny that they are almost invisible. Kiwis have small heads, almost no neck, and very round bodies covered in coarse brown feathers. In truth, kiwis look sort of like hairy footballs!

8. What is the main idea of this passage?
    Ⓐ There are several kinds of unusual, flightless birds.
    Ⓑ Ostriches and emus are very similar in appearance.
    Ⓒ The kiwi is the strangest of all flightless birds.
    Ⓓ Birds that can't fly defend themselves by kicking.

9. Which detail supports the idea that the cassowary is a strange bird?
    Ⓐ It has plumage.
    Ⓑ It can run fast.
    Ⓒ It has claws.
    Ⓓ It has a bony crest on its head.

10. This passage suggests that
   Ⓐ Ostriches are the prettiest of all birds.
   Ⓑ Kiwis are the strangest looking birds.
   Ⓒ Cassowaries are the least dangerous birds.
   Ⓓ Emus are the most unusual birds.

11. The ostrich looks awkward because it
   Ⓐ is the largest living bird.
   Ⓑ grazes on the plains.
   Ⓒ has long legs and a long neck.
   Ⓓ can run 35 miles an hour.

12. From this passage, you can infer that the most dangerous bird is the
   Ⓐ emu.
   Ⓑ ostrich.
   Ⓒ kiwi.
   Ⓓ cassowary.

13. The purpose of this passage is to
   Ⓐ tell an entertaining story about birds.
   Ⓑ explain why some birds cannot fly.
   Ⓒ describe the animals of Australia.
   Ⓓ give information about birds.

14. Which sentence states an opinion?
   Ⓐ Kiwis look sort of like hairy footballs!
   Ⓑ The ostrich can run up to 35 miles an hour.
   Ⓒ Emus defend themselves by kicking.
   Ⓓ The ostrich is the largest living bird.

15. What is the main difference between emus and ostriches?
   Ⓐ their size
   Ⓑ their speed
   Ⓒ their awkward appearance
   Ⓓ their way of defending themselves

16. Which sentence states a fact?
   Ⓐ The ostrich has beautiful plumage.
   Ⓑ Emus weigh about 120 pounds.
   Ⓒ Kiwis look like hairy footballs.
   Ⓓ Cassowaries are bold birds.

Placement Test
Grade 6

The Grade 6 Placement Test has two sections and will take about 45 minutes to complete. The chart below shows the sections of the test, the number of test questions, or items, in each section, and the estimated amount of time required for administering each part. You may administer the entire test in several sessions, or you may choose to administer only some parts of the test.

Section	No. of Items	Estimated Time
Vocabulary	20	20 minutes
Comprehension	16	25 minutes
Total	36	45 minutes

Directions for Administering the Test

To begin the administration, have students look at the front cover of the test and follow along as you read directions aloud:

This is a test of reading and vocabulary. For each part of the test, read the directions carefully. Then answer the questions. Mark your answer to each question by filling in the circle beside the answer you choose.

Have students read the sample question by themselves and fill in the circle beside the answer. Give students time to complete the question. Then have a student provide the correct answer. Discuss the sample question with students and make sure they know how to answer the questions. Then have them turn to the appropriate page and begin the test. Tell students which part(s) of the test they should complete and how much time they will have to finish each part.

For Vocabulary, students should read the directions for each part and answer questions 1–20 independently. For Comprehension, have students read the passages and answer questions 1–16 independently.

Directions for Scoring the Test

The Grade 6 Placement Test can be scored by section or by total test. On page 241, you will find the Answer Key for this test. It lists the correct response for each question and, in the chart at the bottom, lists the skill measured by each test item. On page 242, you will find a Student Test Results Chart for this test. Make a copy of the chart for each student and use it to record the student's results on each part of the test.

Using the Answer Key, score the tests by marking each item correct or incorrect. Then:
- add up the number of questions answered correctly in each section;
- record the number correct in the space provided on the Student Test Results Chart;
- add the scores to determine the total test score.

To find the percentage score for each section and the total test, refer to the Scoring Chart on pages 254–255.

Interpreting Test Results

At the beginning of Grade 6, students who achieve a total test score of 80%–90% should receive on level instruction. Students who score 90% or higher should receive beyond level instruction. Students who score lower than 80% should receive approaching level instruction.

Use the scores on each section of the test (Vocabulary and Comprehension) to help make specific instructional plans for each student. For example, a student who scores 80% or higher in Comprehension but only 60% in Vocabulary would benefit from additional instruction that emphasizes vocabulary development. You may also want to refer to the Tested Skills Chart below the Answer Key to identify the skills measured by those items the student answered incorrectly.

If you have students whose scores do not clearly define their weaknesses and strengths, you may need to administer additional assessments. Administer a diagnostic assessment for those students who are significantly below grade level. See page 13 for reference. For students who seem to be significantly above grade level, you may want to administer additional assessments to collect additional information.

Grade 6 Placement Test
Answer Key

Vocabulary

1. b	11. a
2. c	12. c
3. a	13. c
4. b	14. a
5. c	15. b
6. a	16. a
7. a	17. b
8. b	18. d
9. a	19. b
10. a	20. c

Comprehension

1. b	9. d
2. c	10. b
3. b	11. b
4. d	12. c
5. c	13. a
6. a	14. a
7. b	15. b
8. a	16. a

Tested Skills	Item Numbers
Vocabulary	
Context Clues	1–4
Multiple-Meaning Words	5–8
Synonyms and Antonyms	9–12
Prefixes and Suffixes	13–16
Root Words	17–20
Comprehension	
Analyze Character and Setting	10, 16
Make Inferences	11, 15
Main Idea and Supporting Details	1, 2
Sequence of Events	3, 12
Cause and Effect	7, 13
Evaluate Author's Purpose, Point of View	6, 14
Compare and Contrast	4, 8
Distinguish Between Fact and Opinion	5, 9

Name _____ Date _____

Grade _____

Student Test Results Chart
Grade 6

Test Section	Number Correct	% Score	Notes
Vocabulary	/20		
Comprehension	/16		
Total	/36		

Additional Assessments Indicated:

_____

_____

Placement/Instructional Decisions:

_____

_____

Student's Name _____ Date _____

Teacher's Name _____ Grade _____

Placement Test
Grade 6

This is a test of reading and vocabulary. For each part of the test, read the directions carefully. Then answer the questions. Mark your answer to each question by filling in the circle beside the answer you choose.

Sample

Read the sentence. Find the meaning of the underlined word.
Mark your answer.

When Uncle Jed <u>released</u> the fish he had caught, it quickly swam away.
The word <u>released</u> means

Ⓐ washed.

Ⓑ let go.

Ⓒ spoke about.

Ⓓ followed.

Vocabulary

A. Read each sentence. Find the meaning of the underlined word or words. Mark your answer.

1. The store had a variety of flowers, and I could not choose my favorite from so many. The word variety means
   - Ⓐ a kind.
   - Ⓑ a selection.
   - Ⓒ lack.
   - Ⓓ a vase.

2. I was reluctant to do my homework but my mom said I had to. The word reluctant means
   - Ⓐ unable.
   - Ⓑ happy.
   - Ⓒ unwilling.
   - Ⓓ excited.

3. Because the school forbids it, I cannot use my cell phone in the classrooms. The word forbids means
   - Ⓐ does not allow.
   - Ⓑ encourages.
   - Ⓒ causes.
   - Ⓓ does not know.

4. When Leo was carrying the couch up four flights of stairs, Polly realized that he had strength like a superhuman. This sentence means that
   - Ⓐ Leo has super powers.
   - Ⓑ Leo's strength is incredible.
   - Ⓒ Leo is a different kind of human being.
   - Ⓓ Leo's strength is normal.

5. An umbrella will shield you from the rain. In this sentence, the word shield means
   - Ⓐ a metal piece of armor.
   - Ⓑ a police officer's badge.
   - Ⓒ protect.
   - Ⓓ sun visor.

6. Many scouts were out at the varsity basketball finals this year. In this sentence, the word scouts refers to people who
   - Ⓐ look for talented athletes.
   - Ⓑ are sports fans.
   - Ⓒ spy on other people.
   - Ⓓ belong to a club.

7. I wrote down in my journal whatever <u>impressed</u> me during the day. In this sentence, the word <u>impressed</u> means

Ⓐ affected.

Ⓒ stopped.

Ⓑ stamped.

Ⓓ annoyed.

8. Jana filled her <u>canteen</u> with water before she set out on her hiking trip. In this sentence, the word <u>canteen</u> means

Ⓐ small kitchen.

Ⓒ small restaurant.

Ⓑ container.

Ⓓ glass.

B. Choose the best answer to each question. Mark your answer.

9. We saw a <u>spectacular</u> view when we reached the top of the mountain. Which word means the **same** as <u>spectacular</u>?

Ⓐ magnificent

Ⓒ ordinary

Ⓑ colorful

Ⓓ strange

10. There is a <u>shortage</u> of muffins in the cafeteria today. Which word means the **same** as <u>shortage</u>?

Ⓐ lack

Ⓒ number

Ⓑ basket

Ⓓ supply

11. She <u>inquired</u> about the time. Which word means the **opposite** of <u>inquired</u>?

Ⓐ answered

Ⓒ forgot

Ⓑ asked

Ⓓ talked

12. In some schools, certain styles of clothing are <u>banned</u>. Which word means the **opposite** of <u>banned</u>?

Ⓐ forbidden

Ⓒ allowed

Ⓑ admired

Ⓓ followed

13. The washing machine is <u>malfunctioning</u>. The word <u>malfunctioning</u> means

Ⓐ working properly.

Ⓒ not working properly.

Ⓑ useless.

Ⓓ of little importance.

14. The paper supply in our school office seems <u>limitless</u>. The word <u>limitless</u> means
   - Ⓐ without limit.
   - Ⓑ up to a limit.
   - Ⓒ with a limit.
   - Ⓓ under the limit.

15. The <u>abandonment</u> of his ship was necessary for his survival. The word <u>abandonment</u> means
   - Ⓐ without abandoning.
   - Ⓑ the act of abandoning.
   - Ⓒ able to abandon.
   - Ⓓ abandoning again.

16. It is <u>unreasonable</u> to expect students to stay quiet during outdoor recess time. The word <u>unreasonable</u> means
   - Ⓐ without reason.
   - Ⓑ using reason.
   - Ⓒ with reason.
   - Ⓓ beyond reason.

17. Which word most likely comes from the word *dicere*, meaning "say"?
   - Ⓐ dice
   - Ⓑ dictator
   - Ⓒ produce
   - Ⓓ cheer

18. Which word most likely comes from the word *gyr*, meaning "turning"?
   - Ⓐ gypsy
   - Ⓑ gymnasium
   - Ⓒ gymnast
   - Ⓓ gyroscope

19. Which word most likely comes from the root word *graph*, meaning "write"?
   - Ⓐ rapid
   - Ⓑ autograph
   - Ⓒ grapevine
   - Ⓓ grateful

20. Which word most likely comes from the word *eruptum*, meaning "to burst forth"?
   - Ⓐ crust
   - Ⓑ entrust
   - Ⓒ erupted
   - Ⓓ syrup

Comprehension

Read each passage and answer the questions that follow.

Quicksand

When you hear the word *quicksand*, what image comes to mind? You probably picture someone up to the waist in wet sand, screaming for help. In fact, quicksand can be very dangerous. People and animals have sunk into quicksand before and never escaped. However, the more you know about quicksand, the safer you will be.

First, quicksand is really just ordinary sand. It isn't some sort of strange hungry beast. Quicksand forms when water seeps up from underneath a layer of fine sand. The water pushes the grains of sand apart and makes the sand loose. This loose sand will not hold up a heavy weight.

Quicksand usually forms along the banks of rivers, at the seashore, or under slow-moving rivers and streams. It only forms when water flows upward through the sand, not over it. If you are in a place that tends to have quicksand, it's a good idea to carry a large stick. As you walk, poke the ground in front of you to be sure it's firm.

Let's suppose that you happen to step into some quicksand. The best way to deal with it is to stay calm. You may sink, but you won't sink quickly. You will have time to try several ways to get out. First, drop anything you might be carrying that adds weight, such as a backpack. Then try walking out—making slow and steady movements with your legs. If this doesn't work, the best thing to do is lie back and float. It's even easier to float on quicksand than on regular water.

Of course, you will want to call for help. If help is nearby, it's best simply to wait. If help is not nearby, then continue to lie on your back but make slow, rolling movements toward the edge of the quicksand. When you feel solid ground underneath, you can stand up.

Some animals seem to know how to avoid sinking down into quicksand. Mules, for instance, fold their legs underneath them and float on their bellies. Cows, on the other hand, tend to panic and wave their legs around. This doesn't help them escape. So, if you are ever trapped in quicksand, think like a mule, not like a cow.

1. What is the main idea of this passage?
   Ⓐ Quicksand isn't really made up of sand.
   Ⓑ Quicksand can be dangerous, but there are ways to escape.
   Ⓒ You should poke the ground in front of you with a stick.
   Ⓓ Animals are able to float on quicksand, but humans always sink.

2. Which detail supports the idea that quicksand can be dangerous?
   Ⓐ Quicksand forms when water seeps up from underneath.
   Ⓑ You will have time to try several ways to get out.
   Ⓒ Animals have fallen into quicksand and never escaped.
   Ⓓ Quicksand is really just ordinary sand.

3. If you get caught in quicksand, what should you do first?
   Ⓐ Wave your arms and legs quickly.
   Ⓑ Drop anything heavy that you are carrying.
   Ⓒ Fold your legs underneath you.
   Ⓓ Poke a stick into the ground in front of you.

4. How is quicksand different from regular sand?
   Ⓐ It is darker.
   Ⓑ It is more dense.
   Ⓒ It is warmer.
   Ⓓ It is looser.

5. Which sentence states an opinion?

   Ⓐ Quicksand forms when water seeps up from underneath a layer of fine sand.

   Ⓑ People and animals have sunk into quicksand before and never escaped.

   Ⓒ Quicksand is a strange hungry beast.

   Ⓓ Quicksand forms along the banks of rivers, at the seashore, or under slow-moving rivers and streams.

6. The author's main purpose in this passage is to

   Ⓐ give information about quicksand.

   Ⓑ tell an entertaining story.

   Ⓒ persuade people to avoid quicksand.

   Ⓓ explain how quicksand forms.

7. Why should you drop anything heavy if you are stuck in quicksand?

   Ⓐ The heavy object in the sand might help push you out.

   Ⓑ Carrying more weight on your body will cause you to sink faster.

   Ⓒ You need your arms free to wave them in the air.

   Ⓓ The drop sound might be heard by someone who can help.

8. How is the mule's reaction to quicksand different from a cow's reaction?

   Ⓐ Mules fold their legs and float on their bellies.

   Ⓑ Mules wave their legs around.

   Ⓒ Mules sink immediately.

   Ⓓ Mules panic and splash their legs around.

The Train Track Mystery

"What's this?" wondered Jenna. She held up a piece of track from a child's train set. A gleam from the track had caught Jenna's eye as she waited in the city train station for her aunt and cousins to arrive.

"Jenna, over here!" cried Aunt Carrie. Jenna knew that her four cousins— Brenda, Kelly, Dawn, and Patsy—couldn't be far behind, so she stashed the piece of track in her backpack and headed toward her aunt. "I'll figure this one out later," thought Jenna.

That night, after finishing her homework and making sure her cousins were asleep, Jenna pulled out the piece of track and studied it. She concluded that it must have come from a very old toy train set, and she wondered how it ended up in the city station. Jenna fell asleep holding the piece of track. She dreamed that she was a girl living back in 1920, and although it had been a difficult year for the family, her parents had purchased a train set for her birthday. It was the circus train that she had wanted so badly after seeing it pictured in a catalog.

Jenna woke up early to the racket of her four-year-old cousin Patsy singing "I've Been Working on the Railroad" at the top of her lungs. "So have I," thought Jenna with a smile. She wanted to study the piece of track again and begin solving the mystery, but then she remembered that today was her great-grandfather's 90th birthday. The family was giving him a surprise party, and it was Jenna' s job to find him a present. It had to be something he really wanted and didn't already have, but Jenna had spent a week on this task already and still didn't know what to get.

Suddenly, Jenna had an idea. She would find the owner of the toy train, buy the train, and surprise Great-Grandpa with it. Jenna knew that her great-grandfather liked riding on trains and probably had liked playing with them as a kid, too.

Jenna called every toy store and hobby shop she could find in the local phone book. No one had sold an old train set recently, but one woman suggested she call Depot Antiques. The man who answered the phone there said the track sounded like it had come from an old toy train set he had sold a week before to an older man—a Mr. Samuel Porter. Jenna thanked the man and said goodbye. Then she quickly looked up Mr. Porter in the phone book and called him.

Mr. Porter listened carefully to everything Jenna told him and was quite surprised. He had, in fact, bought the antique train set for his grandson, and one piece was missing when he got it home. Yes, he had passed through the city train station on his way home that day, and perhaps he had dropped the piece of track on the floor and not noticed. Would he sell Jenna the train? Yes, but only for one day. The price? A double birthday party for his grandson, Jeremy, and her great-grandfather. It seemed they had both been born on the same day—85 years apart!

When Mr. Porter and Jeremy arrived that afternoon, it was Jenna's turn to be surprised. Jeremy was just as Jenna had pictured him—an adorable and bright-eyed five-year-old. The surprise was that he was sitting in a wheelchair. Jenna introduced Mr. Porter and Jeremy to the rest of her family, and Mr. Porter said, "Please, call me Sam." Jeremy giggled and handed the train set to Jenna, and then everyone helped to put it together as they waited for Great-Grandpa to arrive.

Great-Grandpa was delighted with the party. He was so pleased to see all of his children, grandchildren, and great-grandchildren—all girls. He joked when he saw Jeremy that it was nice to have another male around. Then he spotted the train set, and his eyes lit up. "The Big Circus Train set! The one I wanted as a boy! How did you know? Where did you find it?"

Jenna explained how she'd found the piece of track and how it had led her to Jeremy and his grandfather. Great-Grandpa seemed to like the story almost as much as the train set. "I love a good mystery," he commented. "You would make an excellent detective, Jenna."

All afternoon, Jeremy sat right next to Great-Grandpa, and the two of them took turns making the sound of a train whistle. All the kids, big and small, took turns running the train. Jenna had indeed gotten Great-Grandpa something he didn't already have and really wanted—a chance to be a kid again and play with the train set of his dreams.

9. Which sentence states a fact?

Ⓐ Great-Grandpa was delighted with the party.

Ⓑ "You would make an excellent detective, Jenna."

Ⓒ She concluded that it must have come from a very old set train set.

Ⓓ Jeremy and her great-grandfather were born on the very same day—85 years apart.

10. What was Jenna's problem?

Ⓐ She had to meet Jeremy.

Ⓑ She needed to find a good birthday present for her grandfather.

Ⓒ She could not find her answers.

Ⓓ She got lost on her way to the train station.

11. What question was Jenna trying to answer?

Ⓐ Who is Jeremy?

Ⓑ Where is the train set that is missing a piece?

Ⓒ Why did she dream about being a girl in 1920?

Ⓓ When will Aunt Carrie and her cousins visit again?

12. Which of these events happened first?

Ⓐ Jenna dreamed about a train set.

Ⓑ Jenna did her homework.

Ⓒ Jenna met her aunt at the train station.

Ⓓ Jenna pulled out the piece of track.

13. Jenna woke up early in the morning because
    Ⓐ her cousin was singing.
    Ⓑ the phone rang.
    Ⓒ a train whistled.
    Ⓓ Great-Grandpa called her.

14. The author's main purpose in this passage is to
    Ⓐ show how the main character solves a mystery.
    Ⓑ share information about different train sets.
    Ⓒ tell about Jenna's special birthday party.
    Ⓓ share a story about how Grandpa and Jeremy met.

15. Why do you think Jenna dreamed of living as a girl in the 1920s?
    Ⓐ She was thinking about her Grandpa's life in 1920s.
    Ⓑ She fell asleep holding a piece of a very old train set.
    Ⓒ She had just read a book about the 1920s.
    Ⓓ She had just learned about the 1920s era in school.

16. Which word best describes Mr. Porter?
    Ⓐ kind
    Ⓑ nervous
    Ⓒ strict
    Ⓓ rude

Scoring Chart

The Scoring Chart is provided for your convenience in grading your students' work.

- Find the column that shows the total number of items on the test.
- Find the row that matches the number of items answered correctly.
- The intersection of the column and the row provides the percentage score.

	TOTAL NUMBER OF ITEMS											
NUMBER CORRECT	4	5	6	7	8	10	15	20	30	40	45	50
1	25	20	17	14	13	10	7	5	3	3	2	2
2	50	40	33	29	25	20	13	10	7	5	4	4
3	75	60	50	43	38	30	20	15	10	8	7	6
4	100	80	67	57	50	40	27	20	13	10	9	8
5		100	83	71	63	50	33	25	17	13	11	10
6			100	86	75	60	40	30	20	15	13	12
7				100	88	70	47	35	23	18	16	14
8					100	80	53	40	27	20	18	16
9						90	60	45	30	23	18	18
10						100	67	50	33	25	22	20
11							73	55	37	28	24	22
12							80	60	40	30	27	24
13							87	65	43	33	29	26
14							93	70	47	35	31	28
15							100	75	50	38	33	30
16								80	53	40	36	32
17								85	57	43	38	34
18								90	60	45	40	36
19								95	63	48	42	38
20								100	67	50	44	40
21									70	53	47	42
22									73	55	49	44
23									77	58	51	46
24									80	60	53	48
25									83	63	56	50
26									87	65	58	52
27									90	68	60	54
28									93	70	62	56
29									97	73	64	58
30									100	75	67	60

Placement Assessment • Grades K–6